cabin

Consonants can stand for sounds at the beginning, in the middle, or at the end of a word.

Write the letter to show where you hear the sound in the picture name.

Write the letter that finishes the word.

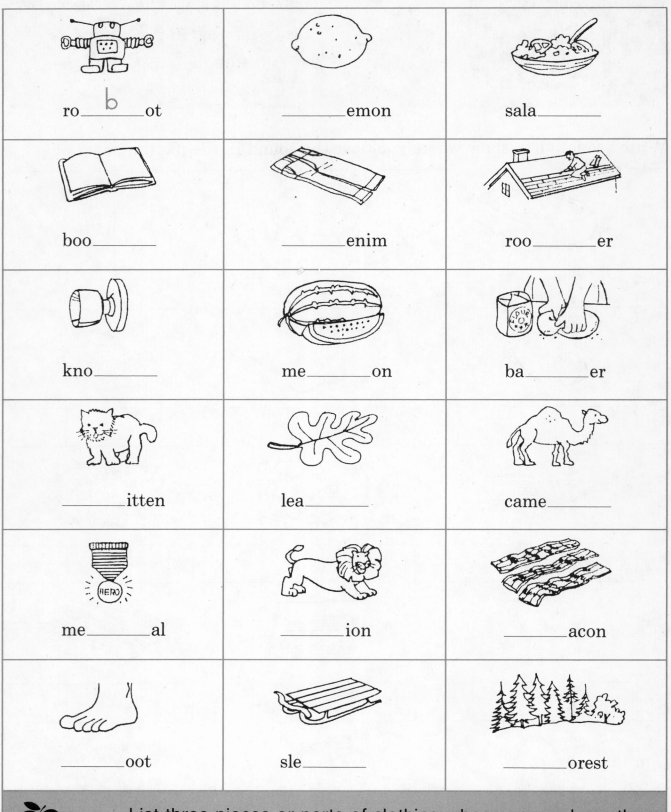

ro __b__ ot

____emon

sala____

boo____

____enim

roo____er

kno____

me____on

ba____er

____itten

lea____

came____

me____al

____ion

____acon

____oot

sle____

____orest

Write the letter to show where you hear the sound
in the picture name.

s ___ s ___ ___	g ___ ___ ___	h ___ ___ ___
r ___ ___ ___	w ___ ___ ___	s ___ ___ ___
g ___ ___ ___	r ___ ___ ___	w ___ ___ ___
r ___ ___ ___	h ___ ___ ___	g ___ ___ ___
s ___ ___ ___	w ___ ___ ___	h ___ ___ ___
r ___ ___ ___	g ___ ___ ___	s ___ ___ ___

Initial, Medial, and Final Consonants   3

Circle the letter to show where you hear the sound.

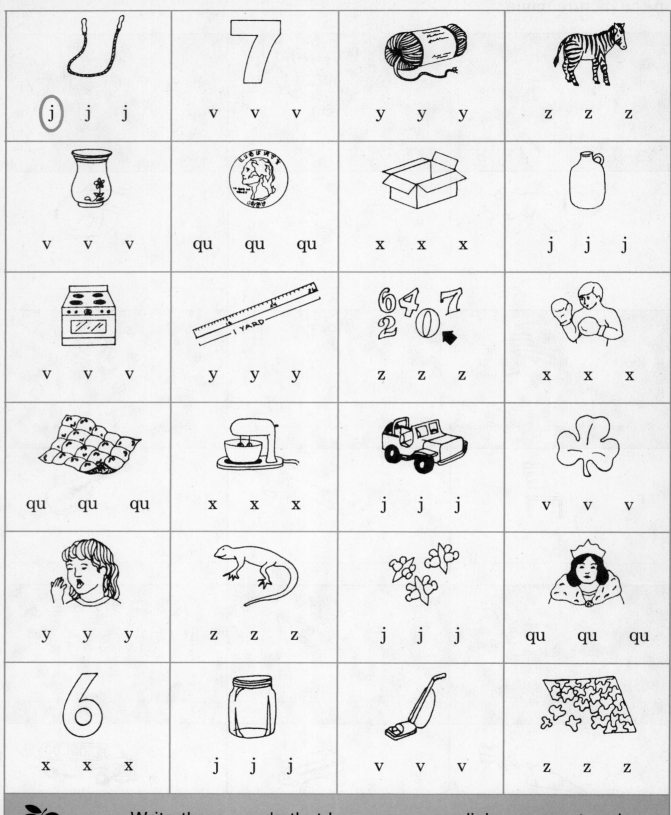

(j) j j	v v v	y y y	z z z
v v v	qu qu qu	x x x	j j j
v v v	y y y	z z z	x x x
qu qu qu	x x x	j j j	v v v
y y y	z z z	j j j	qu qu qu
x x x	j j j	v v v	z z z

Home Study Write three words that have **v** as a medial consonant and three words that have **z** as a medial consonant.

4   Initial, Medial, and Final Consonants

<u>c</u>ity   <u>c</u>ent   i<u>c</u>y

The letter _____ followed by the letters **i, e,** or **y** usually stands for the **s** sound.

Circle the letter for the sound **c** stands for in each word.

(s) / k <u>c</u>ereal	s / k <u>c</u>arrot	s / k pen<u>c</u>il	s / k o<u>c</u>topus
s / k mi<u>c</u>e	s / k <u>c</u>ap	s / k ra<u>c</u>e	s / k <u>c</u>up
s / k jui<u>c</u>y	s / k <u>c</u>oat	s / k lila<u>c</u>	s / k voi<u>c</u>e
s / k musi<u>c</u>	s / k <u>c</u>elery	s / k <u>c</u>ow	s / k <u>c</u>ymbals
s / k <u>c</u>amera	s / k re<u>c</u>ord	s / k pri<u>c</u>e	s / k <u>c</u>eiling

Write the letter **s** in the box if **c** stands for the **s** sound.
Write the letter **k** in the box if **c** stands for the **k** sound.

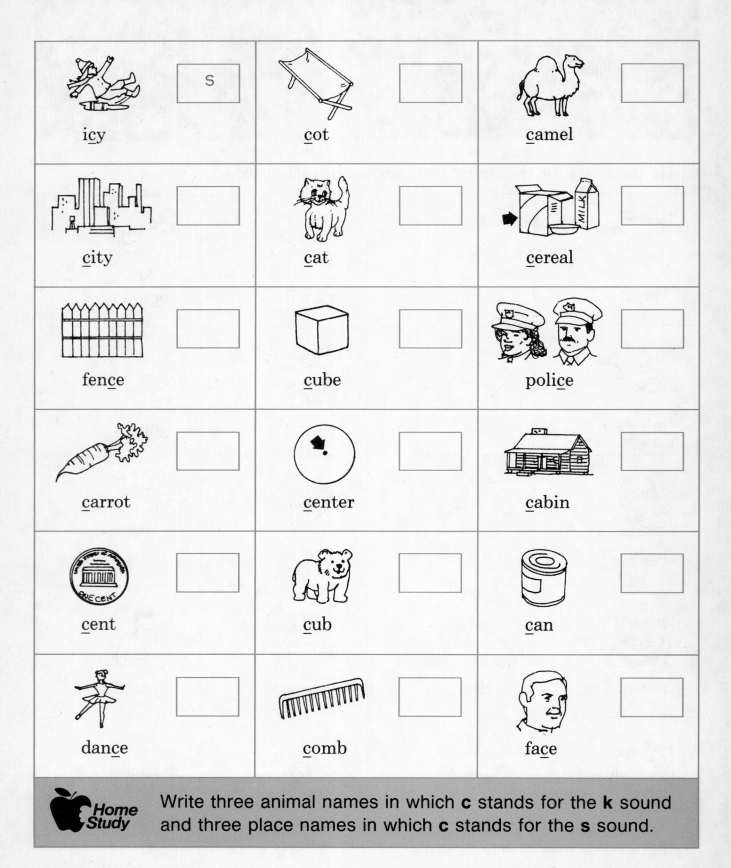

icy — s	cot	camel
city	cat	cereal
fence	cube	police
carrot	center	cabin
cent	cub	can
dance	comb	face

Home Study Write three animal names in which **c** stands for the **k** sound and three place names in which **c** stands for the **s** sound.

cage   giant   gym   bridge

The letter **g** followed by **e, i,** or **y** and the letters **dge** stand for the _____ sound.

Circle the letter for the sound **g** or **dge** stands for in each word.

badge — g ⓙ	gate — g j	orange — g j	edge — g j
wagon — g j	judge — g j	giraffe — g j	germs — g j
hedge — g j	guitar — g j	gentle — g j	rug — g j
gull — g j	ledge — g j	general — g j	goat — g j
gem — g j	page — g j	dragon — g j	engine — g j

Write the letter **g** in the box if **g** stands for the **g** sound.
Write the letter **j** in the box if **g** or **dge** stands for the **j** sound.

hedge — **j**	garden — ☐	organ — ☐
danger — ☐	pig — ☐	cage — ☐
gas — ☐	bridge — ☐	game — ☐
magnet — ☐	stage — ☐	gem — ☐
general — ☐	girl — ☐	gerbil — ☐
judge — ☐	twig — ☐	page — ☐

Home Study Choose one of the pictures whose name has the sound **g** stands for in **stage.** Make up a story using the picture.

8   Hard and Soft **g**

Copyright © 1988 by The Riverside Publishing Company. All rights reserved.

1. sh

2.

3. <u>sh</u>oe

Write the word that names each picture.

ship whip chip	 whip		
thick chick shark			
shop chop thorn			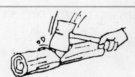
check whale shack			
thin shirt chin			

Initial Consonant Digraphs **sh, wh, ch, th**   9

Read each sentence. Use the letters **sh, wh, ch,** or **th** to finish each word. Then write the word.

It is too cold to wear •orts. __shorts__

There are •erries in the jam. _____

Fred, •isper the reason to me. _____

This •air is made of wood. _____

Did you •op for the party? _____

There were •irty in the class. _____

I want to •eck the answers. _____

The book I want is on the •elf. _____

What do you •ink of that? _____

The play was at the new •eater. _____

This is meat on •eat bread. _____

The milk in the •ermos is cold. _____

Smoke was coming from the •imney. _____

The new •eelchair had a motor. _____

Matt wants to •istle the tune. _____

The •oes are too big for me. _____

The •ip left the dock on time. _____

There are •irteen scouts at camp. _____

How much is the •eese sandwich? _____

Home Study Write two more words that begin with each of the sounds **sh, wh, ch,** and **th** stand for. Use each word in a sentence.

Initial Consonant Digraphs **sh, wh, ch, th**

Write the word that names the picture.

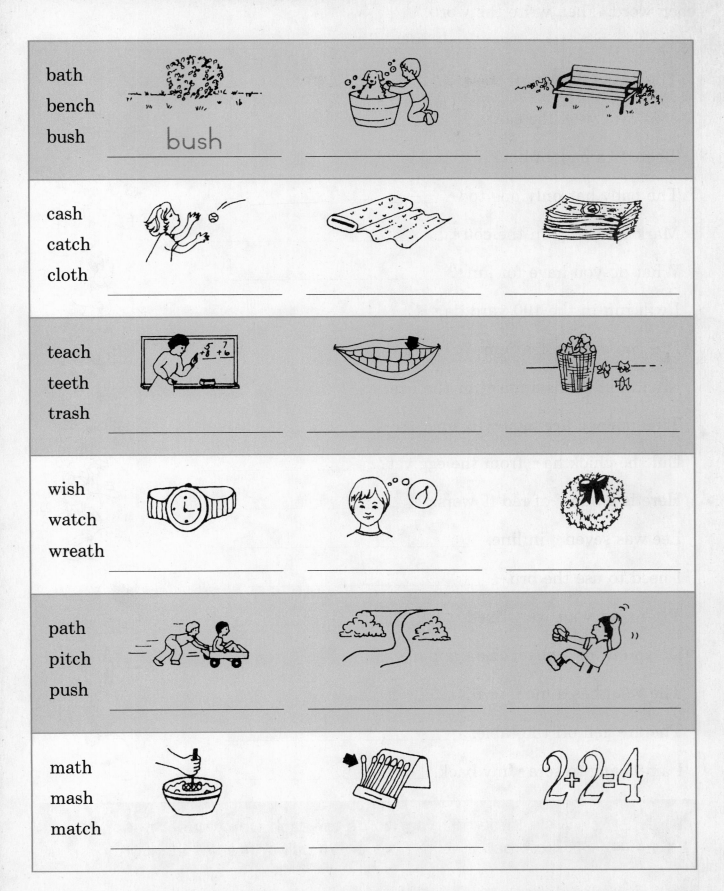

bath bench bush	bush		
cash catch cloth			
teach teeth trash			
wish watch wreath			
path pitch push			
math mash match			

Read each sentence. Use the letters **sh, ch, tch,** or **th** to finish each word. Then write the word.

The bran • broke off the tree. ___branch___

John will wa • the car. _____

There is a pa • of blue in the sky. _____

The baby has only one too •. _____

Mark is sitting on the cou •. _____

What do you have for lun •? _____

I will run in the 100-yard da •. _____

Did you see the fi • jump? _____

My father needs a ma • for the fire. _____

Tina opened her mou • to sing. _____

Did the chick ha • from the egg yet? _____

Here is a bun • of red flowers. _____

Lee was seven • in line. _____

I need to use the bru •. _____

Try to get your wa • fixed. _____

Do you want a pea • or an apple? _____

The wool has a mo • in it. _____

The di • fell off the table. _____

I am trying to scra • my back. _____

 **Home Study** Write three rhyming words for each word: **dash, peach, catch, bath.** Make up a poem using three of the words.

Final Consonant Digraphs **sh, ch (tch), th**

1. st

2.

3. ve<u>st</u>

Use the word part and the letters **st, mp, lk,** or **lf** to write the word.

li •		mi •		wo •	
	list				
si •		po •		la •	
she •		stu •		go •	
bu •		e •		fea •	
cha •		du •		sta •	

Finish both words in each sentence with one of the letter combinations that follows it.

The lo___ck___ on the tru___ck___ door is broken. (ck, sk)

I fe_____ that my be_____ was loose. (mb, lt)

Matt will a_____ Lee to do the ta_____. (lt, sk)

I will cli_____ the tree to cut the li_____. (mb, ck)

If you scare the co_____, it will bo_____. (sk, lt)

The blo_____ is smaller than the bri_____. (ck, sk)

It's so hot, I will either me_____ or wi_____. (lt. sk)

The bottoms of my shoes sti_____ to the de_____. (mb, ck)

He made a ma_____ from the corn hu_____. (sk, lt)

The la_____ had only a cru_____ of food. (lt, mb)

The ta_____ made a cra_____ appear in the wall. (ck, sk)

Where did you tu_____ away that so_____? (ck, lt)

She was nu_____ when she found the to_____. (sk, mb)

You can hear the qua_____ of the du_____. (lt, ck)

Is the qui_____ bigger than the bag of sa_____? (lt, ck)

I hurt my thu_____, and I broke my co_____. (mb, sk)

Gus has already bui_____ one sti_____. (lt, ck)

The computer di_____ was on the de_____. (sk, ck)

Peg is si_____ and Tess hurt her ne_____. (mb, ck)

Home Study — Write ten new words that end with the letters **st**. Draw pictures for at least three of the words.

Read the word after each sentence. Write a rhyming word
to complete each sentence.

Put up the _____ tent _____ as
soon as you get to camp. (sent)

The _____ is a safe
place to put money. (tank)

One _____ is all that
this statue weighs. (round)

Which _____ in the park
do you like best? (thing)

My sister _____ in the
school play. (rang)

Are you going to _____
the apartment? (dent)

He could not even _____
over because of his bad back. (mend)

Tina cannot _____ of
the answer. (sink)

This pot is for the _____
that is in the window. (ant)

A _____ of water would
hit the spot right now. (wink)

If I _____ up, I can
reach the shelf. (grand)

Use this _____ when
you wrap the box. (wring)

I will give you a _____
with moving that couch. (band)

Consonant Combinations **ng, nd, nt, nk**   15

Circle the two letters at the end of each word in the list.
Then use each word to complete a sentence.

s e l e c t   w a s p   s l e p t   w i l d   a c t

There are many _____wild_____ animals
in the zoo.

A _____ was flying around
my head.

Tom will _____ the part of a
sailor in the play.

My mother said I could _____
any shoes I wanted.

The girl was so tired she _____
for ten hours.

g r a s p   t o l d   k e p t   c h i l d   f a c t

The _____ was going to the
ball park with his family.

It is a _____ that squirrels
eat nuts.

I know I _____ you about my
trip to the lake.

Try to _____ the rope as
tightly as you can.

I _____ two sharp pencils
with me for the test.

 **Home Study** Write the letters **ld, pt, sp,** and **ct** at the top of a sheet of paper. List three words ending in each combination.

16   Consonant Combinations **ld, pt, sp, ct**

1. kn
wr

2.

3. <u>kn</u>ife
<u>wr</u>eath

Use the word part and the letters **kn** or **wr** to write the word.

• ist — wrist	• ee	• it
• ing	• ite	• ight
• ock	• ob	• ench
• estle	• uckle	• eck
• ap	• inkle	• ot

Finish both words in each sentence with one of the letter combinations **kn** or **wr**.

Who ___kn___ows how to wear a ___kn___apsack properly?

Clothes get _____inkles if you _____ing them.

I _____elt so long that my _____ee hurt.

The shorter _____estler won the _____estling match.

Here is a bandage to _____ap around your _____ist.

Lee tried the _____ob and then _____ocked.

I _____ow I _____ew the answer at one time.

The greeting is _____itten on the _____apping paper.

When I got the _____ot out, I started _____itting.

The _____iter _____ote the book in three months.

The _____ight only had a _____ife left.

There is a _____ack to _____eading the dough.

The _____en tried to _____iggle into the birdhouse.

Does your _____eecap bother you if you _____eel?

You might scrape your _____uckles if you _____ock.

If I _____ite the _____ong answer, I lose a point.

Jerry _____its coverings for door_____obs.

The terrible _____eck was _____apped around a pole.

The _____ench fell on my _____istwatch and broke it.

Home Study Write three sentences using one **kn** word and one **wr** word in each. Tell a story about one of the sentences.

1.

st

2.

3.

<u>st</u>amp

Use an **s**-cluster and the letters to write each picture name.

• ow • oon • em  spoon		
• unk • an • ile 		
• ale • ump • in 		
• ail • ate • ing 		
• im • oop • ove 		

Consonant Clusters **st, sp, sn, sk, sw, sm, sc**   19

Write a word from the list for each clue.

scoop   spice   skip   stilts

snake   skin   swan   smile

something to walk on _____ stilts _____

a reptile _____

flavors food _____

to take short jumps _____

one's outer covering _____

a beautiful bird _____

shows you are happy _____

helps pick up flour _____

scale   small   switch   skate

snout   stairs   spin   score

take one at a time _____

to change _____

a way to weigh _____

not big _____

move on the ice _____

a pig's nose _____

to twirl _____

tells who's ahead _____

 **Home Study** Think of five things found in the kitchen whose names begin with **st, sp, sn, sk, sw, sm,** or **sc.** Write the words.

Use an **l**-cluster and the letters to write
each picture name.

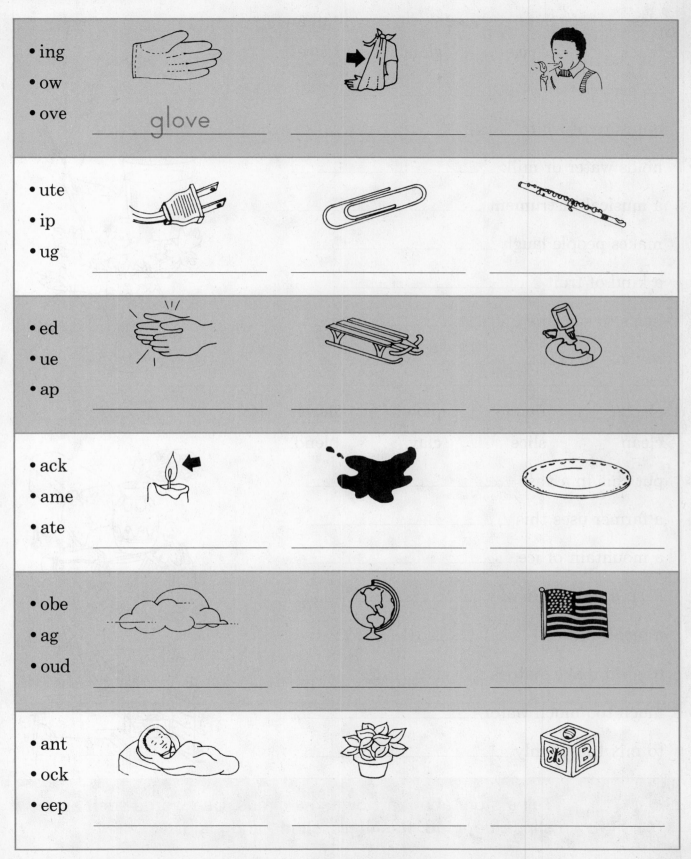

- ing
- ow
- ove

glove _____

_____

_____

- ute
- ip
- ug

_____

_____

_____

- ed
- ue
- ap

_____

_____

_____

- ack
- ame
- ate

_____

_____

_____

- obe
- ag
- oud

_____

_____

_____

- ant
- ock
- eep

_____

_____

_____

Write a word from the list for each clue.

glass	flute	clown	plum
black	please	glance	sleeve

an arm covering ___sleeve___

opposite of white _____

holds water or milk _____

a musical instrument _____

makes people laugh _____

a kind of fruit _____

helps to say this _____

to look quickly _____

glacier	flood	plow	flower
clean	slice	clay	blend

put this in a vase _____

a farmer uses this _____

a mountain of ice _____

keep a room this way _____

a piece of bread _____

used to make statues _____

much too much water _____

to mix thoroughly _____

Home Study Tell a story about a clown in a circus. Use words such as **slip, blue, glad, flashlight, climb,** and **plaid.**

Consonant Clusters **sl, bl, gl, fl, cl, pl**

Use an **r**-cluster and the letters to write
each picture name.

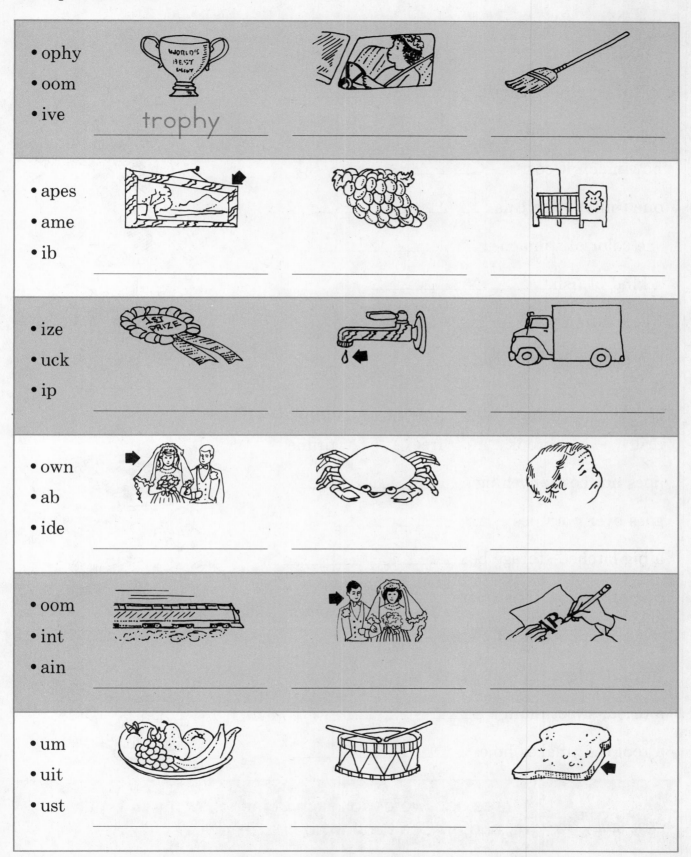

- ophy
- oom
- ive

_____trophy_____

- apes
- ame
- ib

- ize
- uck
- ip

- own
- ab
- ide

- oom
- int
- ain

- um
- uit
- ust

Write a word from the list for each clue.

trout   brush   dream   green

price   fry   crust   brain

to think while sleeping ___dream___

goes with a comb _____

how much it costs _____

one thinks with this _____

the color of spinach _____

a kind of fish _____

to cook in a pan _____

the outer edge of bread _____

---

trunk   drain   gravy   crown

drill   brook   free   prune

does not cost anything _____

goes over potatoes _____

a big latched storage box _____

one might catch fish here _____

it's at the bottom of a sink _____

royal headgear _____

a dried, sweet plum _____

a tool that makes holes _____

 **Home Study** List three new words for each of the following: **tr, br, dr, gr, fr, cr,** and **pr.** Use each word in a sentence.

Consonant Clusters **tr, br, dr, gr, fr, cr, pr**

Use the consonant clusters **tw, scr, squ, spl, spr, str,** and **thr** and the letters to write each picture name.

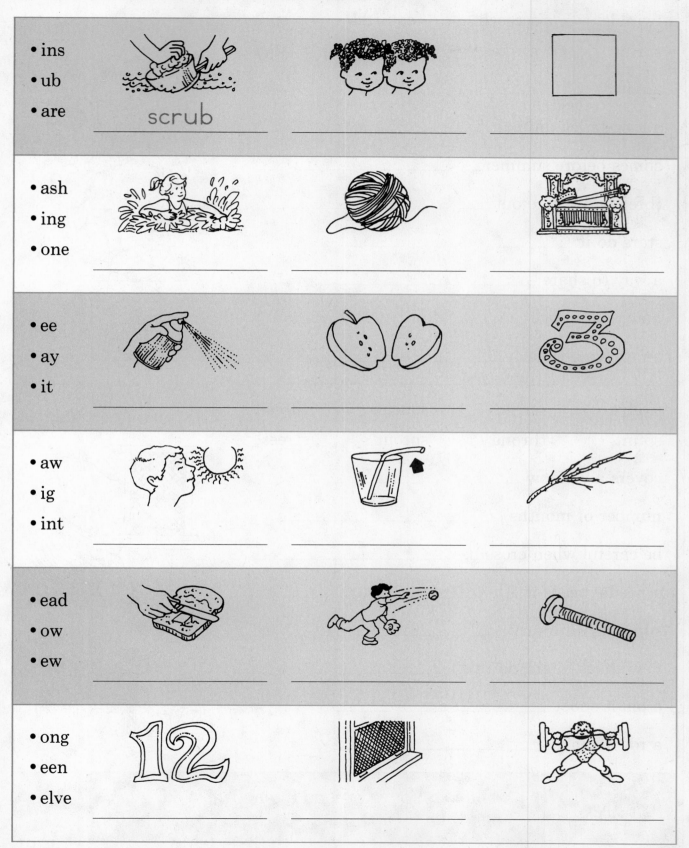

- ins
- ub
- are

scrub
_____

_____

_____

- ash
- ing
- one

_____

_____

_____

- ee
- ay
- it

_____

_____

_____

- aw
- ig
- int

_____

_____

_____

- ead
- ow
- ew

_____

_____

_____

- ong
- een
- elve

_____

_____

_____

Write a word from the list for each clue.

twinkle   screech   squirrel   split

spring   strikes   thrill   squeeze

an owl's call   screech

a long-tailed animal _____

comes before summer _____

three and you're out _____

stars do it _____

a way to share _____

how to get juice _____

an exciting time _____

---

twelve   screen   squeak   thread

splint   throne   sprout   street

covers a window _____

number of months _____

be careful when crossing _____

a needle needs it _____

supports an injury _____

new shoes might do this _____

a plant shoot _____

a royal chair _____

Home Study

Think of things found around the house. Write a list of words that begin with **tw, scr, squ, spl, spr, str,** and **thr.**

Mark the letter or letters that stand for the beginning sound
of the picture names in Rows 1–3. Mark the letter or letters
that stand for the ending sounds in Rows 4–6.

1.

d	n	g	m	g	r	p	b	h	g	t	k
⚪	●	⚪	⚪	⚪	⚪	⚪	⚪	⚪	⚪	⚪	⚪

2.

ch	th	sh	wh	sh	th	ch	sh	wh	wh	ch	sh
⚪	⚪	⚪	⚪	⚪	⚪	⚪	⚪	⚪	⚪	⚪	⚪

3.

wh	th	wr	sh	kn	wr	wr	wh	kn	th	wh	kn
⚪	⚪	⚪	⚪	⚪	⚪	⚪	⚪	⚪	⚪	⚪	⚪

4.

l	b	f	p	h	t	ch	wr	sh	ng	ch	sk
⚪	⚪	⚪	⚪	⚪	⚪	⚪	⚪	⚪	⚪	⚪	⚪

5.

th	nk	ch	mp	wr	tch	st	ck	mb	sk	ck	lk
⚪	⚪	⚪	⚪	⚪	⚪	⚪	⚪	⚪	⚪	⚪	⚪

6.

st	ck	lf	ck	mp	lt	ng	nd	nk	nt	nk	ng
⚪	⚪	⚪	⚪	⚪	⚪	⚪	⚪	⚪	⚪	⚪	⚪

Fill in the oval by the word that has the same beginning sound as the picture name.

1.	○ spill ○ snail ● stop	8.	○ skin ○ sport ○ star	15.	○ sky ○ sweep ○ spot
2.	○ spin ○ swing ○ skip	9.	○ snap ○ smile ○ stump	16.	○ store ○ small ○ score
3.	○ blink ○ sling ○ glass	10.	○ glad ○ bloom ○ slip	17.	○ clay ○ float ○ plum
4.	○ flap ○ cloth ○ play	11.	○ clown ○ trail ○ plow	18.	○ dream ○ brush ○ fruit
5.	○ crib ○ grew ○ dress	12.	○ crust ○ frame ○ floor	19.	○ drink ○ brick ○ prize
6.	○ thrill ○ straw ○ twig	13.	○ spread ○ scrub ○ split	20.	○ twins ○ square ○ strike
7.	○ spring ○ screen ○ stream	14.	○ spread ○ twenty ○ street	21.	○ threw ○ strap ○ splash

The dark word in each sentence is wrong. Find a word
to replace it. Write the word on the line.

1. I read a new **hook** about robots.

   keep   book   _____

2. Please put your **bed** out in the garden.

   sled   had   _____

3. We will have waffles and **boots** for breakfast.

   beams   bacon   _____

4. The zipper on my **jeep** is stuck.

   jacket   jump   _____

5. Would you like a **seashell** for lunch?

   sandwich   baseball   _____

6. Mom can play a **garden.**

   flag   guitar   _____

7. That rabbit is eating all of our **gloves.**

   clover   votes   _____

8. Put the bags into your **dragon.**

   wagon   goat   _____

9. An elephant likes to eat **pencils.**

   pots   peanuts   _____

10. There are six **queens** in the jar.

    beans   jeans   _____

11. A zebra and a walrus were at the **zero.**

    zigzag   zoo   _____

12. Use a **vase** to clean the rug.

    violin   vacuum   _____

In each word, underline the letter that stands for /g/, /j/, /k/, or /s/. Fill in the puzzle. Use the clues and the words in the list.

dragon   cymbals   dog   face

leg   fence   gentle   cat

page   cent   gem   celery

ACROSS

3. not rough or mean
4. the front of a head
5. a penny
6. a green vegetable
8. a monster, in stories

DOWN

1. a sheet of paper
    in a book
2. an animal that meows
3. a jewel
4. put between
    two yards
5. two metal saucers
    that crash together
7. connected to
    a foot
8. an animal that barks

Writing   Write a story about a dragon. Use words from the crossword puzzle. Draw a picture to go with the story.

Unscramble the underlined word in each sentence.
Write the word on the line.

1. Carlos used a <u>hsvole</u> to dig the hole for the rosebush.

   _____

2. We saw the play at the new <u>haeetrt</u> in town.

   _____

3. My sister and I picked a bushel of <u>eishcrer</u>.

   _____

4. Everyone should <u>psirehw</u> in the library.

   _____

5. Look up at a star and make a <u>sihw</u>.

   _____

6. During the holidays, we put a <u>erawht</u> on the front door.

   _____

7. I am helping to cut out a <u>thapc</u> for the quilt.

   _____

8. Would you rather have a banana or a <u>epahc</u> for lunch?

   _____

9. Make sure you walk the dog on a <u>elhas</u>.

   _____

10. One of the <u>ehwels</u> on my bicycle is broken.

    _____

11. Use a <u>hmlebit</u> when you sew the shirt.

    _____

Draw a line between each pair of rhyming words. Then use each underlined word in a sentence. Write the word on the line.

swing	sand
hand	rent
sink	king
tent	slept
act	grasp
crept	drink
clasp	cold
hold	fact
felt	lamp
camp	belt
elf	list
husk	sack
fist	shelf
pack	tusk
milk	thumb
crumb	silk

There is a _____ and a slide in our yard.

_____

Take the _____ from each ear of corn.

_____

Have a _____ of juice with your snack.

_____

I go away to _____ in the summer.

_____

You _____ late this morning.

_____

There is a bread _____ on the floor.

_____

Is that house for sale or _____?

_____

Be sure to take your shopping _____.

_____

Writing Many children go to a summer camp. Write about summer, at camp or at home. Try to use words from this page.

Circle the sentence that tells about the picture. Write the
word in that sentence that begins with a consonant cluster.

We use a plow when it gets too deep.

We use a claw when it gets too deep.

_____

My sister loves her broom.

My sister loves her flute.

_____

Will one blanket be enough for you?

Will one sled be enough for you?

_____

Do you see the scarf outside?

Do you see the smoke outside?

_____

Did you skate in the kitchen?

Did you sweep in the kitchen?

_____

I saw a big spider in the web.

I saw a big snake in the web.

_____

It is fun to walk on swans!

It is fun to walk on stilts!

_____

The dark word in each sentence does not belong.
Write the word by the sentence it belongs in.

1. I have a **prize** brother. _____

2. The log was **street** in two. _____

3. Can you **square** this needle for me? _____

4. **Scratch** the blanket on the bed. _____

5. That shape is a **split.** _____

6. You may win a **twin** in the contest. _____

7. Be careful not to **spread** your hand. _____

8. I live on the next **thread.** _____

1. There is a **gravy** in the wall. _____

2. Mom will **train** us to the store. _____

3. This picture needs a **knife.** _____

4. I have to **branch** a birthday present. _____

5. Put out a fork and **drive** for each person. _____

6. That tree has a broken **frame.** _____

7. Put the **crack** into this bowl. _____

8. Sue catches the **wrap** at eight o'clock. _____

Writing It is fun to enter a writing contest. Write a story to enter in a contest. Make up a list of prizes to win.

a

h<u>a</u>m

Write the letter that stands for the vowel sound in the picture name.

e			

Read the sentence. Draw a line from the unfinished
word to the letter that stands for the vowel sound.
Write the word.

1. I took the yellow b•s.

u
e
_____bus_____

2. Did you water the pl•nt?

i
a
_____

3. We will camp in a t•nt.

e
u
_____

4. Val knows how to sw•m.

o
i
_____

5. The soup is in the p•t.

a
o
_____

6. We sat on a park b•nch.

e
a
_____

7. Lee and Pam like to r•n.

o
u
_____

8. Tim will march in the b•nd.

i
a
_____

9. Cook the meat on the gr•ll.

i
u
_____

10. Peg found a big r•ck.

e
o
_____

11. The beach has white s•nd.

a
u
_____

12. Don took a big st•p.

e
a
_____

Home Study Write **a, e, i, o, u** on cards. Pick a card and say five words
with the short vowel sound that the letter stands for.

c<u>a</u>n<u>e</u>   p<u>ai</u>nt
h<u>ay</u>

The letters _____ + _____, _____, and _____ stand for the long **a** sound in words.

Circle the word that has the same vowel sound as the picture name.

(bat) bait	can cane	rain ran	ham hay
pal pail	pan pane	say sat	tame mat
lake lack	wait what	cape cap	rake rack
pat pay	back bake	tape tap	pad paid
mane man	plan play	aim am	snack snake

Write the word that completes the sentence. Circle
the word with the same vowel sound and vowel pattern
as the word that completes the sentence.

1. I will take a short _____ nap _____ .   (ham)   cane
   cap   nap   paint   hay

2. What did you _____?   ham   cane
   say   day   paint   hay

3. Tom likes to _____ bread.   ham   cane
   lake   bake   paint   hay

4. Can you please _____ for me?   ham   cane
   bait   wait   paint   hay

5. We can _____ in the yard.   ham   cane
   play   clay   paint   hay

6. They must _____ in line.   ham   cane
   grand   stand   paint   hay

7. The money is in the _____ .   ham   cane
   safe   same   paint   hay

8. Did you _____ the letter?   ham   cane
   mail   pail   paint   hay

 **Home Study** Write lists of words that rhyme with the words **cat, day, make, nail.** Make up rhymes with some of the words.

Circle each word with short or long **a.** Write each word under
the picture whose name has the same vowel sound and pattern.

1. (Take) the yellow (cab.)

2. Don't let the rain get in your way.

3. Snap your fingers while you play.

4. Don't wait until it is too late.

5. Stay in this grand hotel.

6. Make this my special day.

7. Save ten stamps for the prize.

8. Stains go down the drain with Whiz.

9. Sail on the big, clear lake.

10. Pay only one dollar to ride on the train.

11. Give your cat one can of Meow Fish.

12. Say yes to the plate of good food.

cab   take

_____   _____   _____   _____

_____   _____   _____   _____

_____   _____   _____   _____

_____   _____   _____   _____

Short and Long **a** Vowel Sounds   39

Read the sentence. Write the name for the picture.
Then circle the symbol that stands for the
vowel sound.

1. Jim walks with a _____ .   cane   a   (ā)

2. We ate some _____ .   _____   a   ā

3. Cows and horses eat _____ .   _____   a   ā

4. Ann will _____ her room.   _____   a   ā

5. Ned put on his _____ .   _____   a   ā

6. I put the food on a _____ .   _____   a   ā

7. Use some _____ on the box.   _____   a   ā

8. Jen has a _____ in her hair.   _____   a   ā

9. Please turn on the _____ .   _____   a   ā

10. Sam made a cup out of _____ .   _____   a   ā

11. Did Jan close the _____ ?   _____   a   ā

12. I can read a _____ .   _____   a   ā

Home Study Say the words **make, pail, mat, say, pat, tape, nail, tap.**
Clap once for a short **a** word. Clap twice for a long **a** word.

tree

leaf

The letters _____ and _____ stand for the long **e** sound in words.

Circle the word that has the same vowel sound as the picture name.

(meet) met	see sell	leap leg	bean bend
stem steam	three the	set seat	net neat
beet bet	teen ten	please pet	wet weed
wed weave	sled seed	seek sent	mean men
get greet	clean cell	step steep	heat hen

Write the word that completes the sentence. Circle
the word with the same vowel sound and vowel pattern
as the word that completes the sentence.

1. I went to ____sleep____ at eight o'clock.

        sleep   sheet

bell   (tree)

leaf

2. They made sand castles on the _____.

        bead   beach

bell   tree

leaf

3. Her house is on the _____ side.

        less   left

bell   tree

leaf

4. "Will you _____ pass the soup?"

        peas   please

bell   tree

leaf

5. The _____ caught the ball.

        seal   seat

bell   tree

leaf

6. Do you _____ some help?

        nest   need

bell   tree

leaf

7. Kim planted a watermelon _____.

        seed   sheep

bell   tree

leaf

8. I put the letter on my _____.

        den   desk

bell   tree

leaf

Home Study Write **kn–, sh–ll, b–d, r–d,** and **thr–** on a sheet of paper.
Add letters that stand for short or long **e** to make words.

Circle the words with a short **e** or long **e** in the slogans.
Write the word under the picture whose name has
the same vowel sound and vowel pattern.

1. (Read) the big (red) book.

2. Sleep great on Snooze flannel sheets.

3. Help save a seal.

4. Let us tell you a tale.

5. Meat and beans are good.

6. Plant a beet seed today.

7. Step up and get a pet.

8. Bring your feet to our ocean beach.

9. Make it neat and clean with our mop.

10. Come to Al's if you need a heel on your shoe.

Read   red

_____   _____   _____

_____   _____   _____

_____   _____   _____

_____   _____   _____

_____   _____   _____

Read the sentence. Write the name for the picture.
Then circle the symbol that stands for the
vowel sound.

1. The [sheep] are in the field. _____sheep_____   e   (ē)

2. Get some ink for this [pen] . _____   e   ē

3. We can plant the [watermelon seed] . _____   e   ē

4. Let's ride in the [jeep] . _____   e   ē

5. Roy put the [tent] up. _____   e   ē

6. Don't feed the [seal] . _____   e   ē

7. Bring a [leaf] to class. _____   e   ē

8. There was a hole in the [net] . _____   e   ē

9. His shoe needs a new [heel] . _____   e   ē

10. She lost her [beads] . _____   e   ē

11. The letter is on the [desk] . _____   e   ē

12. That was a good [meal] . _____   e   ē

Home Study Label three boxes **e, ee,** and **ea.** Find pictures whose names
have the pattern and place them in the proper boxes.

44   Short and Long **e** Vowel Sounds

k_it_e

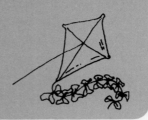

The letters _____ + _____
stand for the long **i** sound in words.

Circle the word that has the same vowel sound as the picture name.

(wrist) write	smile sit	mix mice	hire hit
fig file	list line	ride rid	fin fine
win wise	dig drive	wipe whip	mile mitt
wife with	six side	sip shine	bite bit
while will	him hire	tin time	pit pile

Write the word that completes the sentence. Circle
the word with the same vowel sound and vowel pattern
as the word that completes the sentence.

1. We have a _____ pine _____ tree in our yard.   pig   (kite)

       pine   pile

2. She wore a _____ on her hat.   pig   kite

       pit   pin

3. Can you draw a straight _____?   pig   kite

       line   like

4. The baby needs a _____.   pig   kite

       bid   bib

5. That book costs _____ dollars.   pig   kite

       fine   five

6. Pat got a new _____.   pig   kite

       bike   bite

7. Mark caught three _____.   pig   kite

       fit   fish

8. She _____ a home run.   pig   kite

       hat   hit

 **Home Study** Write **i** and **i + e** on a sheet of paper. List the words from this page under the correct vowel pattern.

Short and Long **i** Vowel Sounds

Circle the words with a short **i** or long **i** in the slogans.
Write the word under the picture whose name has the same
vowel sound and vowel pattern.

1. Get a better (wig) from (Big) Top.

2. Take a hike on your bike.

3. Pull up your chin and grin.

4. Ride on a nice new train.

5. The pine boards work fine.

6. Eat a pile of food at Nine Brothers.

7. Make a wish upon a fish.

8. He has pink lips.

9. Take a hint and plan a trip.

10. Mice are very nice.

wig

Big

Read the sentence. Write the name for the picture.
Then circle the symbol that stands for the
vowel sound.

1. That will cost a [image: dime coin] .   dime   i   (ī)

2. Put the [image: fire] out.   _____   i   ī

3. We saw a [image: pig] at the zoo.   _____   i   ī

4. Ron likes to play on the [image: slide] .   _____   i   ī

5. Put the baby in the [image: crib] .   _____   i   ī

6. Did you put a [image: lid] on the pot?   _____   i   ī

7. Lee has a red [image: bike] .   _____   i   ī

8. Lisa caught a [image: fish] at the lake.   _____   i   ī

9. I have [image: 5] dolls.   _____   i   ī

10. Do you have a safety [image: pin] ?   _____   i   ī

11. They collected [image: pine tree] cones.   _____   i   ī

12. The baby has a [image: bib] .   _____   i   ī

Home Study Write **bike, hive,** and **fine** on a sheet of paper. Write as many words as possible that rhyme with each word.

b**o**ne

c**oa**t

The letters _____ + _____ and _____ stand for the long **o** sound in words.

Circle the word that has the same vowel sound as the picture name.

(coast) cot	cat ox	close cob	load lot
hot home	spoke sock	dot dome	lost loan
stop stone	float fog	hop hope	rode rod
clock coach	pole pop	boast bond	trot tone
rope rot	got goal	job joke	chop choke

Write the word that completes the sentence. Circle
the word with the same vowel sound and vowel pattern
as the word that completes the sentence.

---

1. We took a _____ boat _____ ride.

(coat)   bone

       fox

    roast   boat

---

2. Jan wrote a _____.

coat   bone

     fox

    note   nose

---

3. Put the carrots in the _____.

coat   bone

     fox

    hot   pot

---

4. Roy gave Molly a red _____.

coat   bone

     fox

    role   rose

---

5. Lou had _____ and eggs.

coat   bone

     fox

    toast   toad

---

6. Mark got a new fishing _____.

coat   bone

     fox

    pod   rod

---

7. The _____ knocked over the pail.

coat   bone

     fox

    goat   oat

---

8. Dan put on his old _____.

coat   bone

     fox

    rope   robe

 Home Study Write **o + e, oa,** and **o** on cards. Take a card. Say a word
that has the vowel pattern on the card.

Circle the words with short **o** or long **o** in the slogans.
Write the word under the picture whose name has the same
vowel sound and vowel pattern.

1. Try a (toasty)(oat) cereal.

2. The nose smells a rose.

3. Make a pot of hot stew.

4. Soak your socks in Speedy soap.

5. We hope you bought a Zippy rope.

6. Stop and see the tiny doll.

7. Make a note, please vote.

8. Buy a load of coal at Lee's.

9. Help the toad find a new home.

10. Hop to the top.

toasty

oat

_____   _____   _____

_____   _____   _____

_____   _____   _____

_____   _____   _____

Read the sentence. Write the name for the picture.
Then circle the symbol that stands for the
vowel sound.

1. Rob put the gift in a .   box ⓞ ō

2. Use the to water the grass. _____ o ō

3. The wandered into the yard. _____ o ō

4. He slept on a at camp. _____ o ō

5. The bird sat on the . _____ o ō

6. Father was at the cooking. _____ o ō

7. I like corn on the . _____ o ō

8. Riley has a pet . _____ o ō

9. The dog couldn't catch the . _____ o ō

10. What happened to the ? _____ o ō

11. Jill has a beautiful garden. _____ o ō

12. My sister made a of soup. _____. o ō

Home Study Write **broke, coast, spoke, moan, tone, boast** on a sheet of paper. Underline the letters that stand for the long **o** sound.

cube	fruit
glue	threw

The letters _____ + _____, _____, _____, and _____ stand for the vowel sounds in **cube, fruit, glue,** and **threw.**

Circle the word that has the same vowel sound as the picture name.

muff (rule)	up June	juice plum	new run
dune bun	cute cub	use hug	sub cube
grew rub	pup prune	but flew	clue club
rude cuff	huge hut	duke dull	mug dew
blue puff	true fun	mud fume	tune hum

Vowel Sounds /u/, /ū/, /ü/   53

Read the sentence. Write the name for the picture.
Then circle the symbol that stands for the
vowel sound.

1. My brother plays the ____. _____flute_____   u   (ü)

2. Did you ride the ____? _____   ū   u

3. Take the ____ to Main Street. _____   u   ü

4. I'd like some orange ____. _____   u   ü

5. Sam got a new ____. _____   u   ü

6. Put an ice ____ in my glass. _____   u   ū

7. Jill filled the ____ with water. _____   u   ū

8. ____ and vegetables are good. _____   u   ü

9. The light has blown a ____. _____   u   ū

10. We have to clean the ____. _____   u   ū

11. Use the ____ to measure it. _____   u   ü

12. The red ____ is Bob's. _____   u   ü

Home Study Write words with / u / or / ü / on cards. Pick a card. Say **fluff**
for a word with / u / and **flute** for a word with / ü /.

1. ī

2.

3. fl<u>y</u>

Put an X by each word with the same vowel sound as the picture name.

☐ say   ☒ my

☐ day   ☐ try

☐ yes   ☐ why

☐ yell   ☐ by

☐ bay   ☐ yarn

☐ sly   ☐ yard

☐ pry   ☐ lay

☐ way   ☐ sky

☐ bay   ☐ fry

☐ spy   ☐ yes

Vowel Sound /ī/ (y)   55

Circle the ten words with the long **i** sound. Write one
of those words to complete each sentence.

fit	fly	by	cry	spy
try	pail	dry	may	play
rain	sky	pry	my	sly

1. The birds will ____ south for the winter. _____fly_____

2. Look up at the clear blue ____! _____

3. The desert is very hot and ____. _____

4. The loud noise made the baby ____. _____

5. Ed likes to ____ on us from behind a tree. _____

6. Can you ____ the jar open? _____

7. Ann sat ____ Lou in music class. _____

8. The fox is clever and ____. _____

9. You must ____ to hit the ball. _____

10. I will bring ____ books tomorrow. _____

Home Study Write **y** six times on a sheet of paper. Add consonants
before the **y** to make words. Make rhymes with the words.

1. ē

2.

3. pony
monkey

Put an X by each word with the same vowel sound as the picture name.

☒ happy	☐ try	☐ dry	☐ donkey
☐ my	☐ tiny	☐ sunny	☐ by
☐ why	☐ honey	☐ valley	☐ pry
☐ sky	☐ journey	☐ sly	☐ funny
☐ shy	☐ baby	☐ alley	☐ fry

Vowel Sound / ē / (y, ey)   57

Circle the ten words with the long **e** sound. Write one
of those words to complete each sentence.

honey	funny	they	turkey	cry
shady	valley	city	pulleys	baby
supply	sunny	prey	money	imply

1. The river runs through the _____.   ___valley___

2. How many buildings are in this _____?   _____

3. The day was hot and _____.   _____

4. The _____ sleeps in a crib.   _____

5. Workers used _____ to lift the heavy load.   _____

6. My friend told a _____ story.   _____

7. I need _____ for school supplies.   _____

8. It was _____ and cool under the tree.   _____

9. We had _____ with dressing for dinner.   _____

10. Bees make _____.   _____

Home Study   Write the first line of a funny story using long **e** words from
this page. Tell the whole story to a friend.

1. e

2.

3. br<u>ea</u>d

Put an X by each word with the same vowel sound as the picture name.

☒ leather   ☐ bead

☐ red   ☐ sunny

☐ snail   ☐ steady

☐ thread   ☐ key

☐ sweat ✔   ☐ city

☐ spread   ☐ eat

☐ braid   ☐ ready

☐ feather   ☐ seam

☐ weather   ☐ feel

☐ head   ☐ had

Vowel Sound / e / (ea)   59

Circle the ten words with the short **e** sound. Write one of those words to complete each sentence.

sweater	meet	monkey	steady	dead
leather	eat	feather	easy	head
spread	sweat	ready	weather	silly

1. I found a pigeon _____ in the yard.   *feather*

2. My shoes are made of _____.   _____

3. This street is a _____ end.   _____

4. _____ the cloth on the table.   _____

5. Exercise makes you _____.   _____

6. Get _____ to go.   _____

7. Keep your bike at a _____ speed.   _____

8. Our _____ has been very hot this summer.   _____

9. She held the ball above her _____.   _____

10. I left my woolly _____ at school.   _____

Home Study Find the two words in the list that have both short and long **e**. Write a sentence using both words.

1.	2.	3.
ā ē	8	eigh<u>t</u> c<u>ei</u>ling

Put an X by each word with the same vowel sound as the picture name.

☐ field ☒ sleigh	☐ meet ☐ pipe
☐ seize ☐ size	☐ receipt ☐ bright
☐ free ☐ eighty	☐ neighbor ☐ feel
☐ right ☐ receive	☐ weigh ☐ dry
☐ try ☐ train	☐ team ☐ freight

Vowel Sounds / ā / (eigh), / ē / (ei)   61

Circle six words with the long **a** sound. Underline
four words with the long **e** sound. Write one of
those words to complete each sentence.

receipt	weigh	seven	seized	neighbors
ceiling	sled	freight	fright	receiver
weight	eight	sleigh	prance	tie

1. The Fongs are our _____ .   _____neighbors_____

2. The clerk marked the _____ "paid."   _____

3. Postage is based on the _____ of the box. _____

4. A _____ glides over ice and snow.   _____

5. She replaced the telephone _____ .   _____

6. We waited for the _____ train to pass.   _____

7. The show starts at _____ .   _____

8. He _____ the ball and ran for the goal.   _____

9. My bedroom _____ is white.   _____

10. How much does the watermelon _____ ?   _____

 **Home Study**   Write about some neighbors. Use words such as **eight, ceiling, weigh, receive** in the sentences.

Put an X by each word with the same vowel sound as the picture name.

☒ yield ☐ ripe	☐ paid ☐ piece
☐ brief ☐ die	☐ niece ☐ dime
☐ seize ☐ pie	☐ weigh ☐ lie
☐ dry ☐ reins	☐ trim ☐ shield
☐ untie ☐ need	☐ chief ☐ eight

Circle five words with the long **i** sound. Underline five words with the long **e** sound. Write one of those words to complete each sentence.

point	untied	pie	believe	magpie
piece	shield	die	weigh	weird
chief	yield	dented	lie	risk

1. She wants to be ——— of Police.   _____Chief_____

2. Your shoes are ———.   _____

3. A ——— sign is a yellow triangle.   _____

4. Water the plant or it will ———.   _____

5. This wall will ——— us from the wind.   _____

6. A ——— is a noisy bird.   _____

7. I cannot tell a ———.   _____

8. Use this ——— of chalk.   _____

9. We had chicken pot ——— for dinner.   _____

10. They ——— everything he says.   _____

 **Home Study**   Write the words **yield, tried, tie.** Write at least one rhyming word with the same vowel pattern for each word.

Put an X by each word with the same vowel sound as the picture name.

5

☐ field   ☒ bind   ☐ piece   ☐ fight

☐ sight   ☐ fill   ☐ fright   ☐ swing

☐ mild   ☐ paint   ☐ grind   ☐ weight

☐ sing   ☐ wild   ☐ mind   ☐ niece

☐ sight   ☐ wrist   ☐ sleigh   ☐ might

Vowel Sound /ī/ (ild, ind, igh)   65

Circle the ten words with the long **i** sound. Write one
of these words to complete each sentence.

chief	sight	skin	find	lift
flight	eight	kind	rind	child
field	mild	light	wild	grind

1. He peeled the _____ off the orange.   *rind* _____

2. We enjoyed the _____ weather.   _____

3. She ran at the _____ of lightning.   _____

4. They _____ wheat for flour.   _____

5. The story was about _____ horses.   _____

6. What _____ of books do you like?   _____

7. We saw the geese take _____.   _____

8. The small _____ was sleeping.   _____

9. Please _____ the candle.   _____

10. We may _____ more arrowheads.   _____

Home Study Write long **i** words from this page that can go together in
phrases. An example is **wild flight.**

1. o l

2.

3. r o l l

Put an X by each word with the same vowel sound as the picture name.

☒ hold   ☐ pop

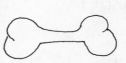

☐ jolt   ☐ soft

☐ fox   ☐ troll

☐ fold   ☐ socks

☐ drop   ☐ told

☐ shock   ☐ cold

☐ cot   ☐ toad

☐ stroll   ☐ spot

☐ lost   ☐ sold

☐ top   ☐ bolt

Vowel Sound /ō/ (ol)   67

Circle the ten words with the long **o** sound. Write one
of these words to complete each sentence.

bolt	sold	stroll	dot	hop
hold	box	toll	knot	told
drop	fold	jolt	troll	mold

1. Don't forget to _____ the door.   bolt

2. They had to pay a fifty-cent _____ .   _____

3. They like to _____ in the park.   _____

4. The _____ was gruff with Billy Goat.   _____

5. Dad _____ us a great story.   _____

6. A quick stop will _____ the riders.   _____

7. We _____ the book at our yard sale.   _____

8. There was _____ on the cheese.   _____

9. _____ the paper in half.   _____

10. Will you _____ my place in line?   _____

Home Study On a sheet of paper, write two sets of three **ol** words, such as **bolt, hold, toll.** Write a sentence using each set.

Fill in the oval under the word that has the same vowel sound
as the picture name.

1. sit   weed   pet

10. trunk   cute   bed

2. time   paid   clip

11. seed   cave   vine

3. foam   kit   take

12. read   juice   nut

4. hole   gate   clue

13. back   hen   lake

5. plan   fire   stay

14. mail   send   peach

6. clock   mat   hose

15. plum   fine   drip

7. lunch   fuse   cape

16. rod   stove   name

8. can   chop   trail

17. late   rule   toad

9. keep   lid   drive

18. stem   nose   pack

Fill in the ovals under the two words whose underlined vowel patterns stand for the vowel sound shown.

1. ē kind ○ piece ●
funny ● hold ○

2. ō colt ○ spread ○
light ○ sold ○

3. ī child ○ told ○
dry ○ niece ○

4. e rind ○ pry ○
thread ○ head ○

5. ā sight ○ weight ○
freight ○ monkey ○

6. ī fly ○ bold ○
only ○ mind ○

7. ā eight ○ brief ○
weather ○ sleigh ○

8. e sky ○ bread ○
feather ○ gold ○

9. ō roll ○ fold ○
baby ○ believe ○

10. ī find ○ berry ○
sleigh ○ night ○

11. e bind ○ tie ○
spread ○ sweater ○

12. ō try ○ jolt ○
cold ○ piece ○

13. ī tie ○ high ○
collie ○ pretty ○

14. ē head ○ cry ○
chief ○ money ○

15. ā weigh ○ my ○
neighbor ○ jolt ○

16. ē sly ○ happy ○
ceiling ○ wild ○

17. ō pie ○ very ○
stroll ○ bolt ○

18. ē honey ○ might ○
field ○ freight ○

Circle the words in the puzzle. Go across or down.
Then write each word to complete a sentence.

tune	T	X	Q	C	H	E	S	T	Z	R
fox	U	P	A	I	N	T	Y	M	O	J
fuse	N	B	C	L	E	Y	F	P	G	U
chest	E	X	K	I	M	B	O	A	T	I
juice	R	M	I	N	X	N	X	N	L	C
pan	T	Q	V	E	K	O	O	Q	P	E
boat	X	B	M	I	Y	T	H	R	S	U
note	D	P	F	U	S	E	Q	H	V	X
line	Q	G	B	E	A	D	S	V	T	Z
beads
paint

1. Use a ruler to draw a straight _____.

2. Pour the batter into the muffin _____.

3. This necklace broke, scattering _____.

4. A _____ lives in our backwoods.

5. Grandma keeps an old _____ in the attic.

6. Our family has a small _____ on the lake.

7. Do you like orange or grape _____?

8. When the lights go out, change the _____.

9. Justin is writing a thank-you _____.

10. Which _____ are you singing?

11. Grandpa likes to _____ winter scenes.

Tell which things go together. Circle a word to complete
each sentence. Write the word.

1. **Many** goes with _____.

few
grew

2. **Coat** goes with _____.

glue
suit

3. **Finger** goes with _____.

thumb
drum

4. **Foot** goes with _____.

cot
sock

5. **Hand** goes with _____.

wrist
weed

6. **Worst** goes with _____.

fed
best

7. **Oranges** go with _____.

pants
apples

8. **Square** goes with _____.

cube
tube

9. **Fire** goes with _____.

joke
smoke

10. **Narrow** goes with _____.

wide
white

11. **Kettle** goes with _____.

dream
steam

12. **Come** goes with _____.

stay
sail

Writing Look at the words which were not circled on this page. Write
sentences using as many of the words as possible.

Read the story. Circle each word in which **y** stands for the long **i** sound and **y** or **ey** stand for the long **e** sound. Write the words in the correct column.

One holiday, I was supposed to get the turkey for dinner.

Mom and Dad gave me the money for it. But on the way to

the store, I lost it in an alley. "Why did this happen?"

I thought. My friends were out playing hockey. I wanted

to play too, not go on this journey. Then a funny thing

happened. In a shady part of the street, I saw a puppy.

It looked shy. "I'll try to get you home," I said. Just

then a man came up. "That's our lost dog," he said,

giving me a reward. I was able to get our holiday dinner

after all!

ē = ey	ē = y	ī = y
_____	_____	_____
_____	_____	_____
_____	_____	_____
_____		

Find a word with the sound shown on the line. Write the word
to complete each sentence.

brief	sleigh	thread	niece
feather	believe	neighbor	freight
weather	field	sweaters	weigh

Sometimes, I help our /ā/ with work. _____

One day, his /ē/ was visiting. _____

She asked me to help for a /ē/ time. _____

"I have to carry the /ā/," she said. _____

"We will put it on my /ā/." _____

"It's the only way to go in this /e/." _____

I didn't /ē/ I could lift a box. _____

"How much do these /ā/?" I asked. _____

"They're as light as a /e/," she said. _____

The boxes held /e/ to sell. _____

They were made of wool and gold /e/. _____

We crossed an open /ē/ on our way to town. _____

Writing Write about a winter sleigh ride. Tell about the weather. Try
to use words from this page.

Circle the /ē/ and /ī/ words in each sentence. Then draw a line
from the sentence to the picture it goes with.

Ann gave a piece to her niece.

The weather is mild for this flight.

Did you receive a receipt for the package?

Do not get pie on your tie.

Lie down and look at the ceiling.

Is there enough light for clear sight?

Wind the clock, but do not grind the gears.

"The night is wild," said the child.

Write the words on the lines to complete the poems.

stroll   jolt   colt

When Jo rode the _____,

It gave her a _____.
She said:

"Next time I'll go for a _____ instead."

fold   roll   folder

older   hold   troll   scroll

A very small _____

Had a very big _____.

He decided to _____ it up.

But each time he got _____,

The paper would _____,

And he wound up _____ —

But with a _____.

cold   gold   sold   bold   told

A sign said: "To the _____ —

All this land will be _____.

You may farm, or find _____, so do so.
If you don't, you'll be left

Way out in the _____,

And I'll say I _____ you so."

Writing Write a story or some more lines of poetry to continue a poem on this page. Draw a picture to go with the writing.

Apply/Extend: Vowel Sounds

1. _____ **2.** _____ **3.** _____

är

st<u>ar</u>

Write the letters that stand for the vowel sound in the picture name.

	ar a sh___ar___k		ai ar c_____t
	ar a f_____n		ai ar j_____
	a ar p_____k		ar a b_____nk
	ar a g_____den		ai ar ch_____t
	ar ay tr_____		ai ar f_____m
	ar ai h_____p		a ar p_____th
	a ar t_____get		ar ai c_____ve
	ar ay b_____n		ar a c_____t
	ar a pl_____nt		ar ay c_____d

Circle the word that matches each meaning.
Write the word on the line.

shines at night _star_ _____	(star) stay	something to wear _____	card scarf
a place to grow vegetables _____	fast farm	used to show words _____	chart chat
how a tabletop feels _____	had hard	used to fix torn pants _____	patch park
a small boy _____	lard lad	a large fish _____	shack shark
a home for animals _____	barn bank	is done to a dog's head _____	pat part
used to catch fish _____	bait bark	used to carry things _____	cat cart
not nearby _____	far fan	to cut meat _____	card carve
a cover for the head _____	hat harp	how it looks at night _____	dark dart

 **Home Study** Write the word **start** on a piece of paper. Then write under it the words from this page that rhyme with it.

1. _____   **2.** _____   **3.** _____

ôr      c<u>or</u>n

Write the letters that stand for the vowel sound in the picture name.

	ar or st___or___k		or o p_____t
	or ar s_____t		o or p_____t
	o or c_____d		or ar st_____y
	or o t_____ch		or ar h_____se
	or o sp_____t		ar or t_____n
	o or th_____n		or o st_____m
	ar or p_____ch		o or b_____x
	or ar st_____e		ar or rep_____t
	o or c_____t		or ar sh_____t

Circle the word that matches each meaning.
Write the word on the line.

an animal to ride _horse_	hose (horse)	used for light _____	torch tone
how fire feels to you _____	horn hot	strong wind and rain _____	stone storm
a large bird _____	stork stove	something like a frog _____	toad torn
one who works with clay _____	potter sport	a place to shop _____	stone store
what ships sail out of _____	pot port	to jump up and down _____	hop born
used to tie things _____	cord cone	arrange in order _____	sort spot
a thing that is dug _____	report hole	the opposite of **long** _____	toe short
something read or told _____	stop story	found on a rose stem _____	thorn throne

 **Home Study** Choose six words from this page. Make up riddles such as: "What is sharp and has a horn?"

1. ėr

2.

3.
f<u>e</u>rn
b<u>ir</u>d
t<u>ur</u>tle

Write the letters that stand for the vowel sound in the picture name.

er e	h__er__d	or ir	c_____cus
ur u	h_____t	ir i	k_____t
ur u	br_____sh	ir i	tw_____l
ir ar	f_____st	u ur	t_____key
e er	b_____nch	er e	p_____ch
ir i	cl_____p	ur u	f_____
er e	g_____ms	u ur	p_____mp
i ir	d_____t	er e	ch_____ck
e er	cl_____k	ur or	c_____ve

Circle the word that matches each meaning.
Write the word on the line.

cause sickness ____germs____	(germs) gems	mud _____	dine dirt
an animal's coat _____	fur fun	where a bird stands _____	perch pen
to cause pain _____	hut hurt	for travel on water _____	ship shirt
needs a drink _____	third thirsty	works in a store _____	click clerk
a kind of bread _____	bun burn	solid _____	fin firm
turn around fast _____	twirl twin	to work for _____	serve set
a large bird to eat _____	turn turkey	part of a song _____	verse pen
difficult to bend _____	stir stiff	used for carrying money _____	put purse

 **Home Study**

Find three or more pairs of er, ir, or ur words that can be used together to describe something, such as first curve.

1. ãr

2.

3. sq<u>ua</u>re
h<u>air</u>
b<u>ear</u>

Write the letters that stand for the vowel sound in the picture name.

	are ar	f___are___		ar air	ch_____
	ar are	p_____k		ear ar	t_____
	air ar	rep_____		ar ear	p_____
	are ar	sh_____		ear er	f_____n
	are ar	d_____k		air ar	st_____s
	ar are	sp_____		ar air	g_____den
	air ar	f_____		are ar	b_____
	ar ear	st_____		er ear	w_____
	ar air	p_____		ar are	c_____

Circle the word that matches each meaning.
Write the word on the line.

two of a kind		looks long at something	
_____pair_____	(pair) pan	_____	tear stares
a large wild animal	bear bait	to go fast	hurry hare
sent for a birthday	care card	what we breathe	air cane
used to sit on	chain chair	a piece of fruit	pear play
money for a bus ride	fare fun	an extra thing	pare spare
for going up and down	stairs star	have on the body	wind wear
play by the rules	for fair	center of an apple	core care
give part to another	share tear	without a cover	bar bare

Home Study Find five pairs of words on this page. Use the words in a sentence, such as "She rode on the **bear's bare** back."

Vowel-**r** (are, air, ear)

1. _____ **2.** _____ **3.** _____

ėr
ir

earth
ear
deer

Write the letters that stand for the vowel sound in the picture name.

ear ar l___ear___n		or eer c_____n	
ear er r_____		eer er p_____ch	
er eer sh_____		ear or s_____ch	
ear er sp_____		er eer h_____d	
ir ear f_____		eer er ch_____	
eer er st_____		ar ear h_____d	
ar ear p_____l		ear er b_____d	
eer er cl_____k		ar eer b_____n	
ear ar sm_____		or ear _____n	

Circle the word that matches each meaning.
Write the word on the line.

a fast running animal _____deer_____	dove (deer)	hair on a man's chin _____	beard bed
want greatly _____	yearn yarn	has feathery leaves _____	fort fern
twelve months _____	hear year	listen to _____	hear hug
a nearly white gem _____	pint pearl	not easy _____	hard heard
close by _____	near neat	a call of praise _____	churn cheer
lion's home _____	deer den	to find out _____	learn lean
drive a car _____	steer stern	used to hold things _____	weary hand
work for something _____	earn burn	much loved _____	dear darn

 **Home Study** Make two columns. Label one **earth** and the other **ear**. Write **ear** words in the columns according to the vowel sounds.

1. ô

2.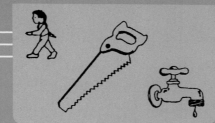

3. walk
saw
faucet

Circle the symbol that stands for the vowel sound.

ⓞ̂ ō o	ô ō o	ô ō o
ô ō o	ô ō o	ô ō o
ô ō o	ô ō o	ô ō o
ô ō o	ô ō o	ô ō o
ô ō o	ô ō o	ô ō o

Choose a word with the same vowel sound as **walk** to name
each picture. Write the word.

call	draw	toy	car	thaw	faucet
sauce	dish	bird	hawk	tool	saucer
phone	auto	creep	tap	saw	crawl
gravy	melt	small	ball	tiny	sketch

faucet

_____

_____

_____

_____

_____

_____

_____

_____

_____

_____

_____

Choose ten words from the word list and write sentences.
Circle the words that have the vowel sound in **walk.**

Choose a word from the box to complete each phrase.
Write the word.

pass the _____ salt _____		lawn
the lion's _____		salt
water the _____		small
large or _____		paw
a telephone _____		claws
_____-headed		saw
the cat's _____		call
hammer and _____		bald
_____ a rocket		false
true or _____		daughter
son and _____		faucets
hot and cold _____		launch
_____ the ball		law
chicken _____		caught
_____ and order		hawk
spring and _____		fall

Choose the word that makes sense in the sentence and has the vowel sound in **walk, faucet,** and **saw.** Write the word.

nap yawn	When I'm sleepy, I _____ yawn _____.
awnings curtains	That house has striped _____.
cheep squawk	Did you hear the chickens _____?
hold haul	That truck can _____ big loads.
fawn animal	Look at the spotted _____!
chalk paper	Teachers use _____.
never always	He is _____ on time.
caution care	Use _____ crossing the street.
stalk stem	The flower is on a slim _____.
Don Paul	_____ is at the door.
pause stop	Let's _____ for a minute to rest.
large tall	That is a very _____ building.

Home Study

Make up a story using at least five words that have the vowel sound in **walk, faucet,** and **saw.** Tell it to a friend.

Vowel Sound / ô / (al, au, aw)

1. ou

2.

3. cl<u>ou</u>d

cl<u>ow</u>n

Circle the symbol that stands for the vowel sound.

ô (ou) ō	ô ou ō	ô ou ō
ô ou ō	ô ou ō	ô ou ō
ô ou ō	ô ou ō	ô ou ō
ô ou ō	ô ou ō	ô ou ō
ô ou ō	ô ou ō	ô ou ō

Vowel Sound / ou / (ou, ow)   91

Choose a word with the same vowel sound as **cloud** and **clown** to name each picture. Write the word.

cow	pouch	shout	flower	owl	scout
boy	nose	yell	ground	house	pocket
mob	hit	dress	snout	animal	rose
bird	land	gown	pound	crowd	home

snout

_____

_____

_____

_____

_____

_____

_____

_____

_____

_____

_____

Make twelve word cards with **ou** or **ow** words. Sort the cards into stacks labeled **cloud** and **clown.**

Choose a word from the box to complete each phrase.
Write the word.

a coyote's _____howl_____	round
a _____ noise	found
the _____ table	loud
lost and _____	howl

the wise old _____	sour
short _____ sound	bow
take a _____	vowel
a _____ lemon	owl

a fluffy, dry _____	How
_____ do you do?	spout
the teapot's _____	towel
_____ and then	now

a water _____	showers
cat and _____	bouncing
April _____	tower
a _____ ball	mouse

Choose the word that makes sense in the sentence and has the vowel sound in **cloud** and **clown.** Write the word.

about for	What is this meeting _____ about _____ ?
couch sofa	Let's sit on the _____.
eyes mouth	Open your _____.
fowl bird	A turkey is a _____.
strong powerful	That is a _____ horse.
bark growl	Did your dog _____?
south north	We traveled _____.
fish trout	Mom caught a _____.
frown cry	What made the baby _____?
eyebrow face	I hurt my _____.
along out	Luis wants to go _____.
tan brown	My new coat is _____.

Home Study Find out what kinds of birds are called fowls. Make a report with pictures.

1.

ou
u

2.

3.

cl<u>ou</u>d

c<u>ou</u>ple

Circle the symbol that stands for the vowel sound.

mouse (ou) / u	southern ou / u	blouse ou / u
double ou / u	proud ou / u	country ou / u
mouth ou / u	tough ou / u	count ou / u
touch ou / u	couch ou / u	rough ou / u
scout ou / u	bounce ou / u	young ou / u

Choose the word that makes sense in the sentence and has the same vowel sound as the underlined word. Write the word.

bug mouse	A _____mouse_____ got in the <u>house</u>.
northern southern	We had <u>fun</u> in _____ Florida.
sound noise	They heard a <u>loud</u> _____.
enough four	Are there _____ <u>cups</u> for us?
faucet spout	Water pours <u>out</u> of the _____.
thick tough	I can't <u>cut</u> the _____ piece of meat.
Push Touch	_____ this button to go <u>up</u>.
time trouble	He took the _____ to do the <u>puzzle</u>.
boot trout	She pulled a _____ <u>out</u> of the stream.
country weather	This is sunny _____!
saw found	I _____ it on the <u>ground</u>.
around into	We ran _____ the <u>house</u>.

 Home Study Label a sheet of paper with the directions North, South, East, and West. Underline the word that has / ou /.

Vowel Sound / ou /, / u / (ou)

1.   ou
          ō

2.

3.   cl<u>ow</u>n
         sn<u>ow</u>

Circle the symbol that stands for the vowel sound.

bowl — ou / (ō)	town — ou / ō	owl — ou / ō
growl — ou / ō	mow — ou / ō	trowel — ou / ō
elbow — ou / ō	frown — ou / ō	shadow — ou / ō
crown — ou / ō	arrow — ou / ō	pillow — ou / ō
blow — ou / ō	flower — ou / ō	bow — ou / ō

Choose the word that makes sense in the sentence and has the same vowel sound as the underlined word. Write the word.

snow powder	The wind will <u>blow</u> the _____ snow _____.
fast slow	We are <u>going</u> too _____!
bowl scoop	Use the _____ on the <u>low</u> shelf.
shovel trowel	She dug up the <u>ground</u> with a _____.
flower growing	He is <u>proud</u> of his _____ garden.
crown bow	We <u>found</u> a paper _____.
willow pine	I <u>know</u> that is a _____ tree.
towel pillow	Where is the <u>brown</u> _____?
school show	Let's <u>go</u> to the _____.
power lights	In the storm, the _____ went <u>out</u>.
hawk crow	That _____ was flying <u>low</u>.
now soon	I want to go <u>out</u> _____.

 **Home Study** Make a list of at least eight words in which **ow** stands for long **o**. Write sentences using the words.

1. ü
ù

2.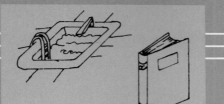

3. p<u>oo</u>l
b<u>oo</u>k

Circle the symbol that stands for the vowel sound.

hook ü **ù**	stood ü ù	tools ü ù
look ü ù	spool ü ù	moon ü ù
groom ü ù	stool ü ù	hood ü ù
scoop ü ù	cook ü ù	spoon ü ù
school ü ù	wool ü ù	woods ü ù

Choose a word from the box that has the vowel sound the symbol stands for and that names the picture. Write the word.

text	noodles	building	tool	boil	see
cook	board	poodle	hook	wood	cold
booth	book	school	dog	stall	look
stool	hanger	spaghetti	cool	chair	saw

ụ̈   book

ü

ü

ü

ü

ü

ü

ü

ü

ụ̇

ü

ụ̇

 Home Study   Use the words on this page to make two columns. Label one **pool** and the other **book.**

Choose a word from the box to complete each phrase. Write
the word. Then circle the symbol to show the vowel sound.

good	_____spool_____ of thread	ⓤ	u̇
smooth	_____ or bad	ü	u̇
book	a library _____	ü	u̇
spool	rough or _____	ü	u̇

noodle	bride and _____	ü	u̇
stood	lamb's _____	ü	u̇
wool	sat or _____	ü	u̇
groom	chicken _____ soup	ü	u̇

toot	a crowing _____	ü	u̇
crooked	_____ your horn	ü	u̇
mood	straight or _____	ü	u̇
rooster	in a good _____	ü	u̇

choose	Little Red Riding _____	ü	u̇
Hood	hand or _____	ü	u̇
took	_____ a nap	ü	u̇
foot	pick and _____	ü	u̇

Choose the word that makes sense in the sentence and has the same vowel sound as the underlined word. Write the word.

pool brook	There's a ___pool___ near our <u>school</u>.
booth nook	<u>Put</u> the vase in that ___.
tools hood	Hang your ___ on that <u>hook</u>.
book moose	I <u>understood</u> that ___.
brook zoo	He <u>zoomed</u> through the ___.
cook goose	That ___ needs <u>food</u>.
tools wood	We need ___ to build the <u>booth</u>.
zoomed stood	She ___ by the <u>brook</u>.
loop hood	This ___ is made of <u>wool</u>.
gloomy crooked	<u>Look</u> at the ___ road.
hood boots	Don't <u>lose</u> your ___.
spoon cook	We need a ___ for the <u>soup</u>.

Home Study

Write a short poem. Use words from this page that contain the vowel sounds in **pool** and **book.**

102 Vowel Sounds / ü /, / u̇ / (oo)
Copyright © 1988 by The Riverside Publishing Company. All rights reserved.

1. oi

2.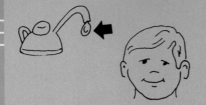

3. o̲i̲
b o̲y̲

Circle the symbol that stands for the vowel sound.

point (oi) ō	**fox** oi o	**soil** oi ō
royalty oi o	**toy** ō oi	**noise** oi ō
boil o oi	**oysters** oi o	**boat** oi ō
joint oi o	**coil** o oi	**choice** oi ō
foil oi ō	**coins** oi o	**poison** ō oi

Choose a word with the same vowel sound as **boy** and **oil**
to name each picture. Write the word.

oysters	dirty	coins	elbow	joyful	toy
doll	child	money	voyage	cook	broil
noise	boy	soiled	happy	trip	foil
sound	joint	destroy	smash	seafood	wrap

joyful

_____

_____

_____

_____

_____

_____

_____

_____

_____

_____

_____

Tell a story about fixing a meal, using such words as **boil**,
broil, **oil**, and **foil**.

Choose a word from the box to complete each phrase.
Write the word.

_____ poison _____ ivy		oink
a pig goes "_____"		avoid
_____ the rush		soybean
_____ fields		poison

a pencil _____		joy
_____ and clams		point
_____ a worker		oysters
_____ or sadness		employ

_____ pests		join
gas and _____		oil
_____ a club		voyage
an ocean _____		annoying

a _____ soldier		choice
a high, squeaky _____		voice
_____ water		toy
made a _____		boiling

Choose the word that makes sense in the sentence and has the vowel sound in **boy** and **oil**. Write the word.

Raymond Joyce	_____ Joyce _____ lives near the mall.
moist damp	That towel is still _____.
ruined spoiled	Rain _____ the picnic.
stowed coiled	The sailors _____ the ropes neatly.
sad joyful	The chorus sang a _____ song.
loyal devoted	Our dog is _____ to us.
Boise Topeka	_____ is a state capital.
poorly royally	Guests are treated _____ here.
noisy loud	The birthday party was very _____.
Detroit Flint	_____ is in Michigan.
staying employed	Mom is _____ at the hospital.
oysters stores	Pearls can be found in _____.

Home Study Study a map of the United States for names of other cities that have the vowel sound in **boy** and **oil**.

1. ə

2.

3. zebr<u>a</u>

a = ə

Circle the vowel sound the underlined letter stands for in the word.

sev<u>e</u>n (ə) ē	muff<u>i</u>n ī ə	bl<u>o</u>ck o ə
sal<u>a</u>d ə ā	r<u>a</u>bbit ə a	childr<u>e</u>n ē ə
b<u>a</u>lloon ā ə	pil<u>o</u>t ə ō	cact<u>u</u>s ū ə
l<u>i</u>on ə ī	barr<u>e</u>l ē ə	cab<u>i</u>n ə ī
circ<u>u</u>s ə ū	t<u>e</u>nt ə e	carr<u>o</u>t ō ə
kitch<u>e</u>n ə ē	m<u>u</u>sic ū ə	rob<u>i</u>n ə ī

Circle the word in each sentence that has the schwa sound. Write the word. Then underline the **a**, **e**, **i**, **o**, or **u** that stands for the schwa sound.

We saw a (zebra) in a zoo. _____zebr<u>a</u>_____

Two dogs chased a balloon. _____

We have a large cactus in our store. _____

Sue liked her canoe ride. _____

Mia solved her problem. _____

Our band was in a parade. _____

My aunt makes a good salad. _____

We stored corn in a barrel. _____

Tom showed me his album. _____

That lion pawed at our door and roared. _____

We bought a bushel of pears. _____

We watched a clown eat raw turnips. _____

 **Home Study** Write a sentence using as many schwa words from this page as possible. Underline the schwa words.

Think of the vowel sound that the underlined letters stand for in the word in dark type. Fill in the oval under the word with the same vowel sound.

1. earn

beard   heard   sheer
○   ●   ○

9. chair

car   bear   harm
○   ○   ○

2. farm

harp   happy   plate
○   ○   ○

10. enough

sound   rough   doubt
○   ○   ○

3. early

fear   learn   steer
○   ○   ○

11. cactus

mount   sour   walrus
○   ○   ○

4. found

howl   tough   mow
○   ○   ○

12. weary

cheer   earn   pearl
○   ○   ○

5. pear

perk   scar   bare
○   ○   ○

13. hard

stare   repair   dark
○   ○   ○

6. clear

yearn   earth   dreary
○   ○   ○

14. kitchen

carrot   bent   pillow
○   ○   ○

7. care

hear   fern   fair
○   ○   ○

15. cloud

double   spout   crow
○   ○   ○

8. wear

ear   hair   learn
○   ○   ○

16. sheer

perch   pearl   near
○   ○   ○

Think of the vowel sound that the underlined letter or letters stand for in the word in dark type. Fill in the oval under the symbol for that vowel sound.

1. blouse ō ô ou ○ ○ ●	**9. straw** ô ō o ○ ○ ○	**17. hook** ū o u̇ ○ ○ ○
2. gown ô ou ō ○ ○ ○	**10. groom** ō u̇ ü ○ ○ ○	**18. first** är ī ėr ○ ○ ○
3. arrow ou ō o ○ ○ ○	**11. barn** a är ā ○ ○ ○	**19. foot** ō o u̇ ○ ○ ○
4. soil ô oi ō ○ ○ ○	**12. spool** o ü u̇ ○ ○ ○	**20. sausage** ō o ô ○ ○ ○
5. report o ō ôr ○ ○ ○	**13. barrel** e ə ē ○ ○ ○	**21. term** är ə ėr ○ ○ ○
6. hook ō u̇ ü ○ ○ ○	**14. wall** ō o ô ○ ○ ○	**22. rough** u ū o ○ ○ ○
7. towel ô ou ō ○ ○ ○	**15. balloon** ā a ə ○ ○ ○	**23. curve** ėr är ü ○ ○ ○
8. moon ü o u̇ ○ ○ ○	**16. toy** oi ô ō ○ ○ ○	**24. bowl** ou ō o ○ ○ ○

Read the story and number the sentences below to show the
order in which they happened. Then circle all of the words
in the paragraph that contain the vowel sound in **star,**
corn, or **fern.**

Uncle Bert is a department store clerk. He will sell you
a turtle, a perch, or a fern for the porch. One Thursday
he had a bad day. First thing in the morning, he burned
his toast. When he got to the store, a purple bird got
out. By the time he caught it, his shirt was torn and
dirty. He planned lunch in the park, but there was a
rainstorm. Then, a little girl took up all his time
asking thirty questions about sharks. When it was
time to go home, his new sports car wouldn't start. It
was a very hard day!

☐ The car wouldn't start.

☐ There was a rainstorm.

☐ A purple bird got out.

☐ A girl asked many questions.

☐ Bert's toast burned.

☐ Bert's shirt got torn and dirty.

Circle the letters in each word that stand for the vowel sound in **ear.** Underline the letters in each word that stand for the vowel sound in **bear.** Put a box around the letters that stand for the vowel sound in **earth.** Use the words to fill in the puzzle.

hear   scare   spear   share

near   care   air   fair

cheer   learn   year   steer   earn

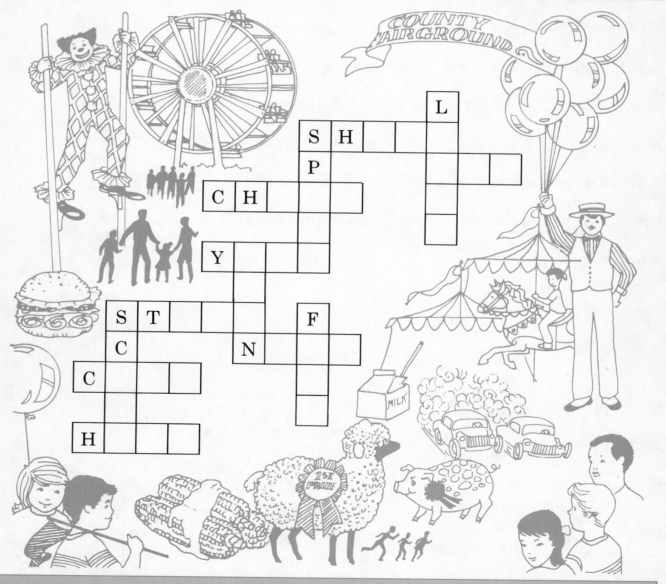

Writing It can be exciting when a fair comes to town. What kinds of fairs are there? Write about going to a fair.

In the stories, questions, and answers, underline each word that
has /ô/. Circle the answer to each question.

One week, June saw all the leaves come down from a tree.

What caused this to happen?

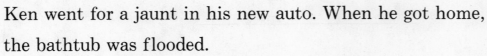

It was sunny.

It was fall.

It was rainy.

Ken went for a jaunt in his new auto. When he got home,

the bathtub was flooded.

What happened?

Ken left the faucet on.

Ken went for a drive.

Ken made dinner.

Henry is very small. Henry likes to crawl by the lawn.

Henry carries the newspaper in his jaws.

What is Henry?

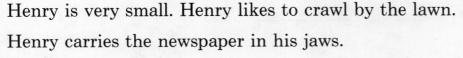

Henry is a hawk.

Henry is a puppy.

Henry is a fawn.

Mary taught her puppy to sit. Each time he did it,

she fed him a sausage. One day, during a lesson,

Mary got a phone call. She left the sausages on

the table. When she came back, they were missing.

What happened?

The puppy sat down.

The puppy answered the phone.

The puppy ate the sausages.

Follow the directions to make new words. Write the words.
Then circle the symbol for the vowel sound.

1. Write the word **growl.**	_____	/ou/	/ō/
Take away **gr.**	_____	/ou/	/ō/
Add **b** to the front.	_____	/ou/	/ō/
2. Write the word **ouch.**	_____	/u/	/ou/
Add **c** to the front.	_____	/u/	/ou/
Change **ch** to **ple.**	_____	/u/	/ou/
3. Write the word **trouble.**	_____	/ou/	/u/
Change **tr** to **d.**	_____	/ou/	/u/
Change **le** to **t.**	_____	/ou/	/u/
4. Write the word **arrow.**	_____	/ō/	/ou/
Add **sp** to the front.	_____	/ō/	/ou/
Change **arrow** to **out.**	_____	/ō/	/ou/
5. Write the word **vow.**	_____	/ou/	/ō/
Change **v** to **c.**	_____	/ou/	/ō/
Change **c** to **cr.**	_____	/ou/	/ō/
6. Write the word **blow.**	_____	/ō/	/ou/
Change **bl** to **fl.**	_____	/ō/	/ou/
Add **er** to the end.	_____	/ō/	/ou/

Writing   Use the words on this page to make a simple crossword puzzle. Write meaning clues for the words.

Choose a word with /oi/, /u̇/, or /ü/ to complete
each sentence. Write the word on the line.

1. Matt wants someone to _____ him. /oi/   employ
                                                      hire

2. Sherry has a French _____. /ü/   dog
                                               poodle

3. _____ to the one you want. /oi/   Point
                                                Walk

4. This sweater is made of _____. /u̇/   cotton
                                                    wool

5. There is a red _____ in the barn. /ü/   rooster
                                                      hen

6. We will cross a little _____ nearby. /u̇/   brook
                                                         stream

7. _____ starts tomorrow! /ü/   Class
                                           School

8. Did you ever eat an _____? /oi/   oyster
                                                egg

9. I need one more _____. /oi/   cent
                                            coin

10. Hang your coat up on that _____. /u̇/   hook
                                                      hanger

11. Did all the flowers _____ already? /ü/   bloom
                                                        die

12. Sara has a new _____ house. /oi/   toy
                                                  white

13. Frank will _____ dinner for us. /u̇/   fix
                                                     cook

14. Grandpa is turning the _____. /oi/   soil
                                                    dirt

Unscramble each word with /ə/. Write it on the line
to complete the sentence.

Gram lives in an old log **bcian.**

_____

It has a living room and a **tihcnek.**

_____

Gram sleeps on a **faos** in the living room.

_____

She also keeps an **narog,** which she plays.

_____

Gram used to be a **scimu** teacher.

_____

I like to look at Gram's photo **balmu.**

_____

It has many pictures of her **lihcrdne.**

_____

Now Gram lives alone with her pet **batrbi.**

_____

There is a **tcsuac** growing outside her house.

_____

There is a **subelh** for vegetables by the door.

_____

Sometimes there are **pnirtus** in it.

_____

Gram eats them with **cbano.**

_____

In her shed is an old sewing **hamcnie.**

_____

She sews quilts and carries them in her **gwnao.**

_____

Writing Write a story using **across, seven, cotton, robin, walrus.**
Circle the letter that stands for /ə/ in each word.

116   Apply/Extend: Vowel Sounds

1. rain
+ coat

2.

3.
raincoat

Circle two words that can make a compound. Write the word.

(fish) hat (star) *starfish*	snow hen storm _____	tap any one _____
bed like time _____	sea shore nose _____	leg place fire _____
suit story teller _____	dust rose saw _____	berry black glass _____
some cat how _____	jog base ball _____	side rain fall _____
bone fry wish _____	pop shot corn _____	stick car drum _____

Read each phrase. Add the words in dark type together to make a compound word. Write the word on the line.

a **box** for **sand** sandbox	a **bird** that is **black**
the **bud** on a **rose**	a **pan** that holds **dust**
a **tub** to take a **bath** in	a **plane** that goes in the **air**
a **shell** from the **sea**	a **paper** that has **news** in it
a **coat** to wear in the **rain**	a **flake** of **snow**
a **house** for a **dog**	a **brush** for a **tooth**
a **boat** to **row**	a **house** on a **farm**

 **Home Study** Look through a magazine to find words that can be added together to make compounds. Check them in a dictionary.

Draw lines from the first word to the two words to which it can be added to make compounds. Write both compound words.

any	where body house	anywhere anybody
sand	cat paper box	_____ _____
rose	bush hand bud	_____ _____
snow	ball star flake	_____ _____
tooth	brush paste pot	_____ _____
school	boot book room	_____ _____
shoe	lace horn hat	_____ _____
night	light bed time	_____ _____

Combine the three words to make two compound words. Then write
the two compound words to complete the sentence.

bird   black   berry

A _____ blackbird _____ will eat

a _____ .

flakes   storm   snow

A _____ has many

_____ in it.

air   plane   port

Catch an _____

at the _____ .

lace   maker   shoe

The _____ sold

me a _____ .

bed   room   time

At _____ , I go

to my _____ .

fly   place   fire

The _____ flew

to the _____ .

Home Study Make cards for **school, house, boat, down, town, night, time, light.** Combine the cards to make compounds.

1. I have   **2.** I + 've   **3.** I've

Circle two words that can make a contraction. Write the contraction.

(you) am (are) *you're*	is not they	am not would
us you would	will we is	have am not
not does she	not I are	are I they
am have you	let am us	are that is
they will am	am I does	is will you

Read each sentence. Add the words in dark type together to make a contraction. Write the contraction on the line.

Mother **is not** going.

isn't

We **are** going soon.

_____

I know **he will** play.

_____

There is the camp.

_____

She would like this.

_____

I will do my best.

_____

They **can not** show us.

_____

He knew **we would** come.

_____

Dad hopes **you will** come.

_____

They **do not** play tricks.

_____

I know **it is** mine.

_____

I would find time.

_____

The story **has not** ended.

_____

He had made the cookies.

_____

 **Home Study** Think of contractions not on this page. Write them on a sheet of paper with the two words each stands for.

Draw lines from the two words that can make contractions
with the word in dark type. Write the two contractions.

was it are	**not**	wasn't aren't	
they you am	**would**		
you she here	**is**		
we they she	**are**		
is I were	**not**		
does you he	**will**		
they she I	**have**		
it he you	**is**		

Combine the three words to make two different contractions.
Write the two contractions to complete the sentence.

did   not   was

_____ Didn't _____ you know that

I _____ wasn't _____ there?

we   she   will

_____ come because

_____ all have fun.

not   were   could

They _____ home, so

we _____ study.

would   you   he

_____ like it if

_____ come and visit.

she   is   what

_____ the name of the

book _____ reading?

have   I   they

_____ tried to call,

but _____ never answered.

Home Study Think of contractions not on this page. Write three or more sentences using two of these contractions in each sentence.

1. hat
dish

2.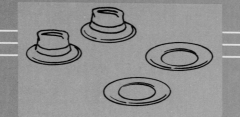

3. hat<u>s</u>
dish<u>es</u>

Draw a line under **s** or **es** to show how the picture name ends.

s <u></u> es	s es	s es
s es	s es	s es
s es	s es	s es
s es	s es	s es
s es	s es	s es

Plurals with **s**, **es**   125

Add **s** or **es** to each word. Write the new word.

hat	hats	book	
box		wish	
rock		inch	
bus		sheet	
day		glass	
ax		brush	
dress		clock	
cup		watch	
bench		nail	
bag		fox	
flash		ship	
fan		match	
dish		hen	
patch		mess	

 **Home Study**

Choose four words that end in **es** on this page. Draw a picture for each one. Write the word under the picture.

Plurals with **s, es**

Think of the picture name. Decide if the picture name needs
s or **es** for the plural ending. Then write it on the line.

We have two _____ .   cats

Look at the many _____ .   _____

Mom has three _____ .   _____

Are there three _____ ?   _____

We need more _____ .   _____

Joan uses two _____ .   _____

Dad washed more _____ .   _____

We've run out of _____ .   _____

Put on those two _____ .   _____

We can use both _____ .   _____

The twins have new _____ .   _____

Where are the extra _____ ?   _____

Choose a word to complete each sentence. Write the word.

bush

bushes   Are there birds in those _____ bushes _____?

bus

buses   The school has a new _____.

wish

wishes   In the story, she had three _____.

box

boxes   What is in all of those _____?

ship

ships   I saw two _____ at the dock.

bench

benches   Let's sit on those _____.

desk

desks   They are working at _____.

cab

cabs   Where is that _____?

class

classes   How many _____ did you have?

Home Study Label two columns **s** and **es**. Spend three minutes writing as many words as possible in each column.

1. walk   **2.** walk + ed   **3.** walked

Add the ending to the word. Write the new word.

fold, ed folded	help, ing
jump, s	look, ed
climb, ing	want, s
work, ing	play, ed
bark, s	eat, ing
clean, s	call, ing

When a word has a final **e,** the **e** is dropped when an ending beginning with a vowel is added. Add the ending in the box to the word. Write the new word on the line.

ed   ed ⟋ ed ⟍ ed ⟋ ed ⟍ ed ⟋ ed

rake ___raked___   smoke _____

close _____   hike _____

smile _____   like _____

bake _____   stake _____

trace _____   spice _____

s   S S S S S S S S S S S

weave _____   write _____

shine _____   make _____

slide _____   flake _____

taste _____   blame _____

ing   ing ing ing ing

leave _____   take _____

save _____   time _____

choose _____   waste _____

tame _____   wake _____

skate _____   shave _____

 **Home Study** Make cards for ten base words on this page and for **s, ed,** and **ing.** Add an ending to each word. Write the new word.

When a word ends in one consonant after a single vowel,
the final consonant is doubled before **ed** or **ing** is added.
Add the ending to the word. Write the new word.

trip, ing tripping	drop, ed
skip, s	step, ing
clap, ed	run, s
trot, s	sun, ed
stir, ing	stop, s
swim, ing	tap, ed
flop, s	spot, ing

When a word ends with a consonant and **y,** the **y** changes to **i** before **es** or **ed** is added, but not before **ing** is added. Add the ending in the box to the word. Write the new word.

ed	

try	tried	copy	
marry		cry	
carry		dry	
study		worry	
fry		hurry	

es	

bury		satisfy	
fly		empty	
spy		deny	
pry		rely	

ing	

imply		occupy	
ply		ferry	
scurry		cry	
copy		study	
worry		spy	

Home Study List pairs of words on this page that rhyme, such as **hurry** and **scurry.** Write a poem, using the rhyming pairs.

1. ful   **2.** help+ful   **3.** helpful

A **suffix** is a word part added to the end of a word to change the meaning. The suffix **ful** often means "full of." Write a new word by adding the suffix to the word in dark type.

has **power**	has **use**
powerful	
causing **harm**	full of **cheer**
full of **care**	likes to **boast**
full of **joy**	full of **color**
full of **doubt**	causing **wonder**
giving **rest**	filled with **fear**
filled with **thought**	likes to **play**

The suffix **less** means "without." Add **less** to the word to complete the sentence. Write the new word.

A baby is help____. helpless	A broken toaster is use____.
Don't be care____ on your bike.	That snake is harm____.
In outer space you're weight____.	Water is a color____ liquid.
In winter, elm trees are leaf____.	Waiting makes me rest____.
This food is taste____!	That small cut is pain____.
Being rude is thought____.	His sleep was dream____.
July was nearly rain____.	It made her feel hope____.

 **Home Study** Look through a book for words with suffixes **ful** and **less.** Make a list of each.

1. er
est

2. tall+er
tall+est

3. taller
tallest

The suffix **er** means "more." The suffix **est** means "most." Write a new word by adding the suffix to the word in dark type.

more than **high** _higher_	most **high**
more than **quick**	most **quick**
more than **slow**	most **slow**
more than **great**	most **great**
more than **low**	most **low**
more than **new**	most **new**
more than **old**	most **old**

Add the suffix **er** or **est** to the word to complete the sentence. Write the new word.

Lee is the fast____ runner in class.

fastest

_____

Luis is tall____ than Don.

_____

That's the quick____ way of all.

_____

Ann is the small____ of the twins.

_____

Pal is a smart____ dog than Rex.

_____

My pencil is short____ than yours.

_____

She is the old____ girl in class.

_____

The sauce is the hot____ I've had.

_____

This price is the low____ in town.

_____

Today is cold____ than yesterday.

_____

Her drum is the loud____ here.

_____

This cloth is soft____ than that.

_____

He works long____ hours than I do.

_____

It's the great____ show I've seen.

_____

Home Study Use words with **er** and **est** to write silly exaggerations such as "My hamster is smaller than an ant."

1. un

2.  un + lock

3. unlock

A **prefix** is a word part added to the beginning of a word to change the meaning. The prefix **un** means "not" or "the opposite of."
Write a new word by adding **un** to each word in dark type.

not **happy** _unhappy_	not **true**
the opposite of **wrap**	the opposite of **buckle**
not **like**	the opposite of **load**
the opposite of **latch**	not **paid**
not **safe**	the opposite of **tie**
the opposite of **pack**	not **equal**
not **lucky**	the opposite of **zip**

Prefixes **un, re**   137

The prefix **re** means "to do again." Choose the word that completes each sentence. Write the word on the line.

Untie
Retie   _Retie_____ the bow to make it straight.

unopen
reopen   This jar is hard to _____!

unpacked
repacked   Jay _____ his bag after his trip.

unlit
relit   Dad _____ the fire when it went out.

Unwrap
Rewrap   _____ the cheese after you slice it.

undo
redo   Laura had to _____ her homework.

unpave
repave   The workers will _____ the road.

Unwind
Rewind   _____ the tape to play it again.

unfolded
refolded   The sheets _____ when they fell.

unnamed
renamed   The school was _____ for the mayor.

unload
reload   Please _____ the bags from the car.

unfilled
refilled   Tara's glass needs to be _____.

 Home Study   Write one of the sentences from this page on a sheet of paper. Then draw a picture to go with the sentence.

138   Prefixes **un, re**

1. dis

2.  dis + connect

3. disconnect

The prefix **dis** means "not" or "the opposite of."
Make a new word by adding the prefix **dis** to the
word in dark type. Write the word on the line.

the opposite of **agree** *disagree*	the opposite of **respect**
not **loyal**	not to **obey**
the opposite of **like**	not **honest**
not to **please**	the opposite of **appear**
the opposite of **comfort**	not to **believe**
not to **approve**	not in **order**
not **content**	the opposite of **mount**

The prefix **pre** means "before" or "beforehand." Choose the word that completes each sentence. Write the word on the line.

unmixed premixed	The batter came _____premixed_____.
unpaid prepaid	All orders must be _____.
disapprove preapprove	My parents _____ of fighting.
Reheat Preheat	_____ the oven before baking.
rearranged prearranged	The wedding was _____.
uncooked precooked	Jan _____ our meal last night.
uncut precut	The puzzle pieces were _____.
unset preset	I _____ my clock last night.
rewrite prewrite	I'll _____ the wrong words.
review preview	We went to the show's _____.
retest pretest	Do the _____ before the unit.
unplanned preplanned	We _____ it on Tuesday.

Home Study Write the word **prearranged** on a sheet of paper. Using the letters from this word, form as many new words as possible.

1. _____ short

2. _____ tall

3. _____

short
tall

Circle and write the **antonym,** or opposite, of the word in dark type.

big	great	small	**cold**	hot	wet
	small _____			_____	
night	time	day	**shallow**	deep	dull
	_____			_____	
slow	fast	tiny	**near**	long	far
	_____			_____	
early	late	large	**tame**	gentle	wild
	_____			_____	
good-by	hello	well	**light**	dark	shy
	_____			_____	
never	not	always	**false**	true	deep
	_____			_____	

Replace the word in dark type in each sentence with
its antonym. Write the antonym on the line.

1. The door is **closed.**

   wood   open   open

2. A mountain is very **low.**

   high   big   _____

3. Would you like a **thick** slice of bread?

   crusty   thin   _____

4. This bed is too **hard!**

   low   soft   _____

5. Our alley is **narrow.**

   dark   wide   _____

6. Our dog is very **old.**

   young   soft   _____

7. We waited in a **long** line.

   small   short   _____

8. That color is **bright.**

   dull   red   _____

9. The clown made me **cry.**

   laugh   sing   _____

 **Home Study** Look in a magazine for words that can have antonyms. List
the words and their antonyms.

1. big

2. large

3. big large

A **synonym** is a word that has the same meaning as another word. Circle the synonym of the word in dark type. Write the word on the line.

speak	move	talk	**angry**	mad	glad
	talk				
finish	end	start	**close**	near	far
cry	run	weep	**dream**	work	wish
shrub	grass	bush	**fast**	quick	slow
glad	funny	happy	**begin**	stop	start
cash	money	truck	**mend**	fix	break

Replace the word in dark type in each sentence with its synonym. Write the synonym on the line.

1. Deb likes to **yell** for her team.

   shout   whisper   _shout_

2. Learning to swim was **easy** for Jim.

   hard   simple   _____

3. I'll be **happy** to help you.

   sad   glad   _____

4. I see a **couple** of birds in the nest.

   pair   crowd   _____

5. Tracy can **repair** the broken toy.

   play   fix   _____

6. I have lived here for **nearly** two years.

   long   almost   _____

7. Don is a **careful** driver.

   safe   poor   _____

8. I have **small** feet.

   large   little   _____

9. Could you please **shut** the door?

   close   open   _____

 **Home Study** Write the words **quick, weep, start, large,** and **talk** on cards. Pick a card and give a synonym for the word on the card.

1. p̃ar

2.

3. pair
pear

Homophones are words that sound alike but have different spellings and meanings. Underline and write the homophone that answers the question.

Does a bear or a bare live in the woods? _____bear_____

Does rein or rain make flowers grow? _____

Can you fall into a whole or a hole? _____

Do you carry water in a pale or a pail? _____

Do you bake bread with flower or flour? _____

Do you tie a not or a knot in a rope? _____

Is a dime ten sense or cents? _____

Do you eat meat or meet? _____

Homographs are words that have the same spelling but different meanings and often different pronunciations. Write the word in dark type that completes both sentences. Then write the letter of the meaning that is used in the sentence.

tear	**bow**	**dove**
A. to pull apart	A. knot tied with a loop	A. plunged into
B. water from the eye	B. bend from the waist	B. a pigeon

wave	**lead**	**wind**	**close**
A. to move the hand	A. soft, gray metal	A. air current	A. to shut
B. a swell of water	B. to guide	B. wrap around	B. near

1. He tied a _____bow_____ on the box. _____A_____

   He took a _____ after the show. _____

2. A _____ rolled down her cheek. _____

   Don't _____ that paper! _____

3. Miners put the _____ in ore cars. _____

   John will _____ the tour. _____

4. Let's _____ the string into a ball. _____

   The _____ blew the shutters open. _____

5. We live _____ to the beach. _____

   Mother said to _____ the door. _____

6. Jill _____ into the pool. _____

   I saw the _____ fly away. _____

7. The _____ washed the boat ashore. _____

   I saw Mark _____ as we left. _____

Home Study Write the words **meat, rode, blue,** and **brake** on a sheet of paper. Write the homophone for each word.

Homophones and Homographs

Fill in the oval under the word that contains the word part underlined in the example word.

1. thought<u>less</u>	joyful ⬭	smarter ⬭	endless ⬮
2. small<u>est</u>	powerless ⬭	tiniest ⬭	grounded ⬭
3. doub<u>tful</u>	restless ⬭	hopeful ⬭	doubted ⬭
4. bench<u>es</u>	caps ⬭	oxen ⬭	matches ⬭
5. marr<u>ying</u>	loading ⬭	hurried ⬭	flies ⬭
6. tub<u>s</u>	boxes ⬭	cars ⬭	he's ⬭
7. wad<u>ed</u>	I'll ⬭	wrapped ⬭	harmful ⬭
8. great<u>er</u>	luckier ⬭	slowest ⬭	helpless ⬭
9. I'<u>ve</u>	you'd ⬭	let's ⬭	you've ⬭
10. tri<u>es</u>	tried ⬭	cries ⬭	hurrying ⬭
11. was<u>n't</u>	didn't ⬭	I'm ⬭	she's ⬭
12. want<u>s</u>	spies ⬭	buses ⬭	packs ⬭

For each section, fill in the oval under every word of the type named.

Compound Words

1. anytime ⬤	sandbox ⬤	catches ◯	sunset ⬤
2. bedroom ◯	crying ◯	schoolhouse ◯	seashore ◯

Prefixes

3. preview ◯	unlike ◯	disappear ◯	sunny ◯
4. person ◯	disagree ◯	preheat ◯	unlock ◯
5. preset ◯	meaning ◯	unpaid ◯	disprove ◯

Synonyms

6. huge ◯	white ◯	small ◯	little ◯

Antonyms

7. I've ◯	tall ◯	short ◯	blackbird ◯

Homophones

8. rode ◯	untrue ◯	road ◯	prepay ◯

Homographs

9. unwrap ◯	project ◯	precook ◯	project ◯

Match two words that can form a compound. Write the number of the first word in the box by the second word. Then write the word to complete a sentence.

1. over		town
2. hill		hive
3. down		heard
4. bee		ball
5. foot		side
6. play		out
7. look		mark
8. lady		ground
9. land		worm
10. earth		bug

A _____ is a small spotted bug.

My brother is on the _____ team.

There is a _____ tower up there.

That tree is a famous _____.

Mom and Dad both work _____.

I _____ them talking.

We like the swings at the _____.

Nectar is stored in the _____.

Sal found an _____ in the dirt.

Running down the _____ is easy.

Use the words in parentheses to form a contraction. Write the contraction on the line in the sentence.

(I am) _____ happy to be here.

(Let us) _____ study after school.

(You have) _____ got to make up your mind.

(are not) We _____ going to wait any longer.

(you are) Are you sure _____ well now?

(What is) _____ that girl's name?

(I will) _____ make sure we're on time.

(would not) You _____ have gone then.

(they are) Do you think _____ coming?

(have not) I _____ got any.

(We will) _____ be right over.

(I have) _____ got to go home now.

(you would) Are you sure _____ like some?

(That is) _____ Peter's car!

(They will) _____ be here tomorrow.

(does not) Sue _____ like this kind.

Writing Write a story using contractions from this page. Be sure to use the words **I, he, she, we, they, us,** and **not.**

150   Apply/Extend: Word Structure

Write a word to complete each analogy.

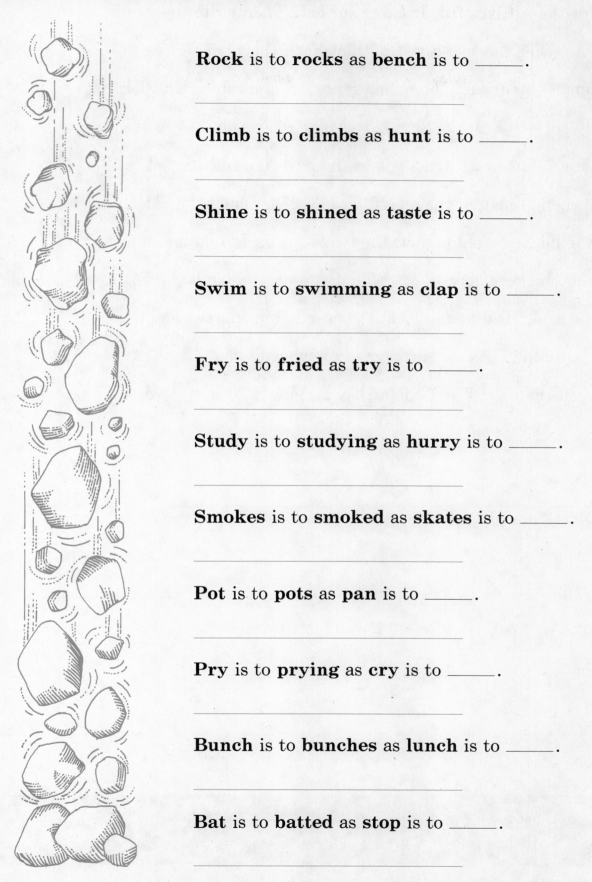

Rock is to **rocks** as **bench** is to _____.

_____

Climb is to **climbs** as **hunt** is to _____.

_____

Shine is to **shined** as **taste** is to _____.

_____

Swim is to **swimming** as **clap** is to _____.

_____

Fry is to **fried** as **try** is to _____.

_____

Study is to **studying** as **hurry** is to _____.

_____

Smokes is to **smoked** as **skates** is to _____.

_____

Pot is to **pots** as **pan** is to _____.

_____

Pry is to **prying** as **cry** is to _____.

_____

Bunch is to **bunches** as **lunch** is to _____.

_____

Bat is to **batted** as **stop** is to _____.

_____

Read the story. Circle the words with the prefixes **un, re, pre,** or **dis** or the suffixes **ful, less, er,** or **est.** Then write the words.

The twins felt joyful at the thought of their trip. Their tickets were prepaid. They had repacked and rebuckled their bags many times. "I dislike having to wait," said Ann. "I get restless." Jan said, "Let's go see the new film preview." Lee gave them a map of the city. "Wasn't that thoughtful?" they said. As the plane soared higher, the twins sat back. It was the fastest jet they had ever been on. "Would you help me unlatch this case?" Ann asked. "Did you unlock it?" asked Jan. But the key had disappeared! The twins disagreed on what to do. They were powerless to open the case. What could they do now?

_____   _____

_____   _____

_____   _____

_____   _____

Writing   Write an ending for this story. Be sure to solve the mystery of the missing key. Tell how the twins' trip went.

Apply/Extend: Word Structure

Break the code for each word. For each letter, write the letter that comes before it in the alphabet. Put A or S on the line to tell whether the word is an antonym or a synonym of the word in dark type.

A B C D E F G H I J K L M
N O P Q R S T U V W X Y Z

S F D B M M
1. I can't **remember** the song's name. _____ _____

O B S S P X
2. Are your shoes too **wide**? _____ _____

T V O S J T F
3. I'll meet you there at **dawn.** _____ _____

T I P V U
4. You don't have to **yell**! _____ _____

S P V H I
5. The cat's fur is very **smooth.** _____ _____

R V J D L
6. I know a **fast** way to go. _____ _____

I J H I
7. The house has **low** ceilings. _____ _____

U B T L
8. This **job** is not easy. _____ _____

E V M M
9. The sun is so **bright** today! _____ _____

Choose a word to fill in the first part of the sentence. Then write its homophone or homograph to fill in the second part.

1. When Bob put on the car's _____,

it caused a carton of eggs to _____ .

2. We'll try to _____ for time

in front of the horse's _____ .

3. I took an apple and a _____,

and put the _____ of them into my bag.

4. I _____ a horse down the

country _____ .

5. It is risky to _____ your camp

in the middle of a sandy _____ .

6. When did the country singer _____

her latest hit _____ ?

7. I had better _____ a minute while

the nurse checks my _____ .

8. Then the nurse checked the _____

in the eyes of her _____ .

rode

stall

pear

break

pupils

weight

desert

brake

record

road

wait

pair

Writing   Use a dictionary to find more examples of homophones and homographs. Use them in sentences.

Apply/Extend: Word Structure

1.

h<u>a</u>m

2.

h<u>a</u>mm<u>e</u>r

3.

ham 1
hammer 2

Write 1 or 2 to show the number of vowel sounds in each word.

knee	1	baseball	2	appear	____
apples	____	basement	____	asked	____
bathtub	____	watch	____	cabbage	____
below	____	sheet	____	berry	____
giraffe	____	palace	____	clock	____
notice	____	fifteen	____	glasses	____
barely	____	pupil	____	tiny	____
inch	____	motel	____	perfect	____
desert	____	children	____	chipmunk	____
cousin	____	brother	____	count	____
blend	____	crawling	____	china	____

Number of Syllables   155

Read each sentence. Underline the words with two
syllables in the sentence. Write the words on the lines.

1. Jane wrote a <u>letter</u> to her <u>sister</u>.

letter   sister

_____   _____

2. I saw a camel and a zebra at the zoo.

_____   _____

3. Do you have a snapshot of the puppy?

_____   _____

4. Let's have bacon and eggs for dinner.

_____   _____

5. Today was sunny and warm, but not hot.

_____   _____

6. Please take out some paper and a pencil.

_____   _____

7. The farm has ducks, chickens, and turkeys.

_____   _____

Home Study Look through a magazine. Find words with two syllables and
copy them on paper.

1.

hammer

2. ha<u>mm</u>er

3. ham / mer

Divide two-syllable words with two like consonants between the consonants. Write the word. Divide it into syllables.

butter	but / ter	funny	_____
ribbon	_____	furry	_____
bottom	_____	pillow	_____
common	_____	letter	_____
tunnel	_____	berry	_____
muffin	_____	carrot	_____
carry	_____	pepper	_____
cotton	_____	tennis	_____
burro	_____	barrel	_____
jelly	_____	runner	_____
pretty	_____	supper	_____
appear	_____	hobby	_____

Read each sentence. Find the two-syllable word with two like consonants that completes each sentence. Write the word and divide it into syllables.

1. Tony won a _____ bal/loon _____ at the fair. prize balloon

2. Please pass the _____. pepper salt

3. The plant has a pink _____. flower blossom

4. May I have the _____ crayon? orange yellow

5. My painting is the _____. finest biggest

6. Put more _____ in the salad. lettuce celery

7. We must _____ to catch the bus. hurry rush

8. Is there a _____ on the bed? quilt pillow

9. The _____ cried for its mother. kitten baby

10. Let's have rice for _____. lunch dinner

11. Climb the _____ to the attic. ladder stairs

12. Jane called Mom at the _____. station office

13. I like _____ more than winter. spring summer

14. Jim felt _____ after the ride. dizzy tired

15. Monday was the _____ day. hottest warmest

 **Home Study** Look in a newspaper. Find three words with two like consonants in the middle. Write a sentence with each word.

1.  basket

2. ba<u>sk</u>et

3. bas / ket

Divide two-syllable words with two unlike consonants between the consonants. Write the word. Divide it into syllables.

walrus	wal / rus	silver	
turnip		picnic	
corner		cartoon	
perfect		carpet	
walnut		organ	
master		doctor	
velvet		rescue	
comfort		carbon	
service		turkey	
target		center	
custard		number	
monkey		timber	

Read each sentence. Find the two-syllable word with two unlike consonants in the middle that completes each sentence. Write the word and divide it into syllables.

1. Lara read a ___chap/ter___ of her book. chapter page

2. We had a _____ to celebrate. dinner party

3. I paste pictures in the _____. album book

4. Do you like _____ on meat? mustard gravy

5. Jill wore a _____ ring. copper silver

6. Jack threw the _____ a fish. walrus seal

7. The play is _____ ready. truly almost

8. We sat on a _____ outside. blanket towel

9. My sister is _____ years old. fifteen twelve

10. Bill took notes on a _____. pad tablet

11. Do you have a _____ of her? picture photo

12. Jo played scales on the _____. piano organ

13. We have a vacation in _____. winter summer

14. The _____ gave enough light. lantern lamp

15. Dad got apples at the _____. market store

Home Study Listen to a song. Write the words with two or more syllables that you hear.

1.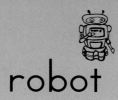

robot

2.

rōbot

3.

rō/bot

Divide words with a long vowel sound in the first syllable after the vowel. Write the word. Divide it into syllables.

pupil	_pu/pil_	final	_____
paper	_____	favor	_____
notice	_____	clover	_____
legal	_____	raven	_____
labor	_____	china	_____
music	_____	meter	_____
human	_____	broken	_____
silent	_____	pony	_____
bison	_____	future	_____
hotel	_____	motor	_____
tiger	_____	total	_____
major	_____	bacon	_____

Read each sentence. Find the word that has a long vowel sound in the first syllable and completes the sentence. Write the word and divide it into syllables.

1. Tom listens to _____mu/sic_____ after school.   music   records

2. We stayed in a _____.   motel   castle

3. What _____ do you like best?   flavor   brand

4. Fold the _____ in half.   paper   card

5. Six _____ two is four.   minus   plus

6. The _____ flew the plane.   captain   pilot

7. Sam stayed in bed with a _____.   headache   fever

8. We go camping to enjoy _____.   walking   nature

9. This letter is the _____ notice.   last   final

10. The _____ came off my shirt.   pocket   label

11. It was a _____ Sunday afternoon.   lazy   sunny

12. I skate when the pond is _____.   solid   frozen

13. A _____ crawled across my floor.   spider   turtle

14. Dad cut the string with a _____.   razor   knife

15. Class was _____ during the play.   restless   silent

 **Home Study** Write a story using several of the two-syllable words on this page. Draw a picture to go with the story.

1.

cabin

2. c<u>a</u>bin

3. cab / in

Divide words with a short vowel sound in the first syllable after the consonant. Write the word. Divide it into syllables.

travel	trav / el	level	_____
clever	_____	never	_____
closet	_____	robin	_____
figure	_____	lemon	_____
lizard	_____	dragon	_____
finish	_____	liver	_____
salad	_____	melon	_____
body	_____	visit	_____
proper	_____	river	_____
damage	_____	magic	_____
punish	_____	model	_____
wagon	_____	novel	_____

Read each sentence. Find the word that has a short vowel sound in the first syllable and completes the sentence. Write the word and divide it into syllables.

1. The king lived in a ___pal / ace___ .   palace   court

2. A _____ fell from the flower.   seed   petal

3. I see _____ chairs in the hall.   seven   eight

4. Our car is more _____ than this.   recent   modern

5. This _____ is close to the sun.   planet   world

6. Put a carrot in the _____ .   meatloaf   salad

7. Her scarf is in the _____ .   desk   closet

8. Do this in the _____ way.   proper   right

9. I saw a _____ at the zoo.   zebra   camel

10. A tent was pitched in the _____ .   desert   sand

11. Please sit in the _____ row.   second   third

12. The boat is made of _____ .   wood   metal

13. Gary will _____ the car.   polish   clean

14. Gail is very _____ at games.   good   clever

15. The wall is very _____ .   thick   solid

 **Home Study** Write new sentences using seven of the two-syllable words on this page. Draw pictures for two sentences.

1. ha__mm__er / ba__s__ket

2. ham/mer / bas/ket

3. ham'mer / bas'ket

Two-syllable words that are divided between two consonants are usually accented on the first syllable. Write each word. Divide each word into syllables. Mark the accent.

pillow	pil'low	circus	
muffin		tennis	
velvet		summer	
office		lettuce	
turnip		monkey	
album		pepper	
serpent		picture	
hurry		doctor	
dentist		tunnel	
pretty		rescue	
timber		blossom	
walrus		garden	

Two-syllable words with one consonant after the first vowel, such as **robot** or **robin**, are usually accented on the first syllable. Divide each word into syllables and mark the accent. Then use the words to complete the story.

melon	motor	visit	cabin
paper	river	fever	future
closet	seven	travel	spider
promise	lizard	station	

A small, green _____lizard_____ lived under an old

rusted _____ near a dried-up

_____ . He went to _____

his friend, a tiny _____ , who lived in a dark

_____ in an old log _____ .

He took a bit of _____ wrapped in

_____ . At a gas _____ ,

he had a drink. "In the _____ , I will

_____ at night," he said. Finally, after

_____ hours, he reached the cabin. Spider was

sick with a _____ and happy to see Lizard.

"I _____ to come back again," said Lizard.

 **Home Study** Write another story about Spider and Lizard. Draw a picture to go with the story.

1. _____
use<u>less</u>
dis<u>use</u>

2. _____
use / less
dis / use

3. _____
use´/ less
dis use´

Divide each word between the base and the prefix or suffix.
Mark the base to show that it is the accented syllable.

near´//est	forceful	preheat
reuse	greenest	distrust
doubtless	hopeless	longer
painful	prejudge	rebuild
displease	fearful	prepaid
richest	unsold	skillful
display	darkest	endless
hardest	pregame	useful
thicker	unseen	deepest
careless	older	remade
dislike	unknown	preflight
peaceful	highest	cloudless

Divide each word into syllables and mark the accented syllable in each word. Then write the word that matches each meaning.

rest′/less	senseless	replant
fastest	cheerful	helpless
coldest	unload	higher
displace	precook	repay

1. without rest _____ restless

2. to pay back _____

3. most fast _____

4. more than high _____

5. foolish _____

6. to cook ahead of time _____

7. to plant again _____

8. happy, pleasant _____

9. to move from its usual place _____

10. to take a load from _____

11. not able to help oneself _____

12. most cold _____

Home Study Look in a book for five words that have the same prefixes or suffixes as the words on this page. Write the words.

Look at each group of words. Fill in the oval by the word that
is divided correctly.

1. ○ ba sket
   ● bas ket
   ○ bask et

2. ○ lant ern
   ○ lan tern
   ○ la ntern

3. ○ all ey
   ○ al ley
   ○ a lley

4. ○ vi sit
   ○ v isit
   ○ vis it

5. ○ den tist
   ○ dent ist
   ○ de ntist

6. ○ ye llow
   ○ yell ow
   ○ yel low

7. ○ tot al
   ○ tota l
   ○ to tal

8. ○ runn er
   ○ run ner
   ○ ru nner

9. ○ t iger
   ○ tig er
   ○ ti ger

10. ○ si ster
    ○ sist er
    ○ sis ter

11. ○ pep per
    ○ pe pper
    ○ pepp er

12. ○ pict ure
    ○ pi cture
    ○ pic ture

13. ○ win dow
    ○ wind ow
    ○ wi ndow

14. ○ co rner
    ○ cor ner
    ○ corn er

15. ○ nev er
    ○ ne ver
    ○ neve r

16. ○ ham per
    ○ ha mper
    ○ hamp er

17. ○ pa per
    ○ pap er
    ○ pape r

18. ○ ra bbit
    ○ rabb it
    ○ rab bit

19. ○ la dder
    ○ lad der
    ○ ladd er

20. ○ ma gic
    ○ mag ic
    ○ m agic

21. ○ sil ver
    ○ si lver
    ○ silv er

Look at each group of words. Fill in the oval by the word that
is accented and divided correctly.

1. ● wag′ on
   ○ wa′ gon
   ○ wag on′

2. ○ sev en′
   ○ se′ ven
   ○ sev′ en

3. ○ ra′ zor
   ○ raz′ or
   ○ ra zor′

4. ○ maj′ or
   ○ ma′ jor
   ○ ma jor′

5. ○ lim it′
   ○ li′ mit
   ○ lim′ it

6. ○ fam ous′
   ○ fam′ ous
   ○ fa′ mous

7. ○ un lock′
   ○ unl′ ock
   ○ un′ lock

8. ○ spid′ er
   ○ spi′ der
   ○ spid er′

9. ○ no′ tice
   ○ not′ ice
   ○ no tice′

10. ○ le vel′
    ○ lev′ el
    ○ le′ vel

11. ○ mi′ nus
    ○ min′ us
    ○ mi nus′

12. ○ nav′ y
    ○ na′ vy
    ○ nav y′

13. ○ med′ al
    ○ me′ dal
    ○ med al′

14. ○ fin′ al
    ○ fi′ nal
    ○ fin al′

15. ○ vis′ it
    ○ vi′ sit
    ○ vis it′

16. ○ hum′ an
    ○ hu′ man
    ○ hum an′

17. ○ pre pay′
    ○ pre′ pay
    ○ prep′ ay

18. ○ rob in′
    ○ ro′ bin
    ○ rob′ in

19. ○ hab′ it
    ○ ha′ bit
    ○ ha bit′

20. ○ flav or′
    ○ fla′ vor
    ○ flav′ or

21. ○ lab el′
    ○ la bel′
    ○ la′ bel

For each blank in the story, pick a word that makes sense and has the number of syllables shown. Write the word on the line. Draw a line between the syllables of each two-syllable word.

Nothing brings out the __1__ of food like eating outdoors. A __2__ in the park or words is a special treat. Pack a __3__ with __4__ sandwiches and potato __5__. Fill a thermos with __6__ and don't forget vegetables— __7__ and __8__. __9__ napkins and __10__ plates and cups are a must. Some __11__ for dessert would be perfect. If there is room, tuck pepper and __12__ into the basket. Is anyone hungry? Now, all we need is a __13__ day.

1. (2 syllables) _____ spices/taste/flavor

2. (2 syllables) _____ snack/picnic/ballet

3. (2 syllables) _____ basket/box/blanket

4. (1 syllable) _____ soup/bacon/ham

5. (2 syllables) _____ skins/salad/butter

6. (2 syllables) _____ cider/radish/milk

7. (2 syllables) _____ beans/rabbit/lettuce

8. (2 syllables) _____ tuna/carrots/corn

9. (2 syllables) _____ Cloth/Paper/Metal

10. (2 syllables) _____ cotton/glass/plastic

11. (2 syllables) _____ fruit/cabbage/melon

12. (1 syllable) _____ sage/salt/mustard

13. (2 syllables) _____ warm/sunny/stormy

Circle the words that have only one syllable. Draw a
line between the syllables of each two-syllable word.
Use the words to complete the puzzle.

pig	tiger	donkey	burro	raccoon
lizard	pony	spider	camel	tortoise
turkey	cow	monkey	goat	rabbit

Writing

Connect two syllables in each box to make a word. There are three words in each box. Then use the words to complete the sentences.

cab ad big bage sal gest	Terry bought the _____ _____ for a _____ .
sis ise prom ter fa vor	I did _____ to do a _____ for my _____ .
pup ket ti py bas ny	The _____ _____ lay in a _____ .
pa cil un per pen der	The _____ is _____ the pile of _____ .
bet sic or ter mu gan	The _____ is _____ when played on the _____ .
kit der res ten lad cue	He needs a _____ to _____ the _____ .
pal low tun ace be nel	Far _____ the _____ was a dark _____ .

The words in dark type must be divided to fit on the lines. Write the first syllable of each word before the hyphen and the second syllable on the next line.

CELEBRATE WINTER
THIS FRIDAY

People couldn't stop talking last week about the _____ -   **notice**

_____ posted on the door of Dr. Hill's _____ -   **office**

_____ . It said there that the school's _____ -   **Winter**

_____ Party will take place on Friday. _____ -   **Seven**

_____ booths are for food or drinks. Hot _____ -   **cider**

_____ is always a favorite. A skating _____ -   **contest**

_____ will be held on the pond, now _____ -   **frozen**

_____ solid. Also, cross-country skiing _____ -   **lessons**

_____ will be given by Ms. Bell. The _____ -   **newest**

_____ thing on the program is a snow _____ -   **person**

_____ contest for kindergarten and _____ -   **preschool**

_____ children. "I think that all the _____ -   **students**

_____ will love it!" said Dr. Hill.

Writing   Write a paragraph about an event at your school. Be sure to divide two-syllable words correctly at the end of a line.

Add accents to the words in the list. Then use the words
to complete the sentences.

use less	mu sic	but ton	bi son	pan da
help ful	riv er	col lar	dis like	re heat
un tied	ar mor	cen ter	cav ern	bun ny

1. My shoes are always _____ _____ _____ _____ _____ /.

2. A knight's _____ _____ / _____ _____ _____ was very heavy.

3. I lost a _____ _____ _____ / _____ _____ _____ from my coat.

4. His advice was _____ _____ _____ _____ / _____ _____ .

5. Piano _____ _____ / _____ _____ _____ filled the air.

6. Many _____ _____ / _____ _____ _____ once roamed the plains.

7. Some people _____ _____ _____ _____ _____ _____ / sports.

8. The Nile is the longest _____ _____ _____ / _____ .

9. Stand in the _____ _____ _____ / _____ _____ _____ of the room.

10. A _____ _____ _____ / _____ _____ _____ is a large cave.

11. A broken tool is _____ _____ _____ / _____ _____ _____ _____ .

12. A turtleneck is a kind of _____ _____ _____ / _____ _____ _____ .

13. I'll _____ _____ _____ _____ _____ _____ / the soup for supper.

14. The _____ _____ _____ / _____ _____ is native to Asia.

15. We gave the baby a stuffed _____ _____ _____ / _____ _____ .

Underline each word with a prefix or a suffix. Write the words on the lines. Divide the syllables and mark the accented syllable of each word you write.

1. Bill was careful to reseal the letter.

_____   _____

2. Be sure to reheat the sauce to make it thicker.

_____   _____

3. I thought the peaceful, quiet road would be endless.

_____   _____

4. I will preheat the oven at the highest temperature.

_____   _____

5. Unlike my cat, my dog is always silly and playful.

_____   _____

6. It will displease me if you are wasteful of paper.

_____   _____

7. I will replace this worthless lightbulb.

_____   _____

8. On the coldest day, the sky was cloudless.

_____   _____

Writing   Write four new sentences using words with prefixes and suffixes. Draw pictures to go with the sentences.